Propelling Beyond Barriers

Evelyn Sharp: No Ordinary Girl

Glenda K Clare

Independent

This novel is dedicated to all women - in the arts, business world, sports, and women's rights who have gone before and busted through the barriers and stereotypes of their day. Women, like Evelyn Sharp, didn't listen to those who would discourage and demean. They found their roads to success and finished the journey.

Contents

    Faithfully writing with integrity, vision, and emotion to
    touch the soul and heart of my readers.

Prologue

A ROLE-MODEL TO YOUNG WOMEN – THEN AND TODAY!

http://glendakclare.com

During a basketball game, athletes drive to the hoops with their eyes on the prize. In football, players push past the goal line and gain the reward. Propulsion is the use of energy or power to achieve one's dreams - no matter the barriers.

Evelyn Sharp pushed past cultural restrictions and the opinions of others. Difficulties or failures did not control her life. During her lifetime, a female's role in life was drastically limited. Women were unable to gain medical degrees, manage corporations, or operate rockets in space. Still today, some dreams of young women and girls remained unattainable and unfulfilled especially for those who don't access to technology.

However stereotypical restrictions or cultural barriers could not deter Evelyn Sharp. The small-town girl, Evelyn Sharp of Ord, Nebraska, achieved a record-making career in aviation. She is a role-model for all young women to be persistent and find a way!

Chapter 1

Dreaming of Clouds

The ten-year-old girl sat cross-legged on the wood floor and brushed the hair from her eyes. Scissors, paste, and paper scraps surrounded a pile of saved clippings and articles. Evelyn tilted her torso close to her collection and studied the columnists' predictions and opinions. "They are picking the wrong horse. Amelia Earhart will win this race." She pressed her lips together. "I just know it."

"Evelyn, you look like a mad scientist." Her mother, Mary Sharp, leaned on the kitchen doorframe and frowned. "You've made a mess of my parlor."

A stack of scrapbooks filled with pages of glued newspaper clippings leaned against a smaller notebook of information from radio broadcasts scribbled in Evelyn's handwriting. "Aww, Mother, I know as much about the pilots as those reporters do, that's for sure!" She raised up on her knees, "Did you know that pilots choose flight jackets based on the plane and weather conditions?"

When her mother shook her head, Evelyn chattered on. "I saw it in Life magazine. Usually pilots wear a jacket, hat, and a pair of goggles. But now that planes fly higher and faster, they need warmer clothes."

"Well, that makes sense."

"Yeah, if a pilot operates in an open cockpit, she wears a leather jacket with tight cuffs, waist band, and a wraparound collar."

"Yes, I've seen those magazine photos of pilots with their scarves billowing in the wind."

"Yeah, but not now, Mama. In an open-cockpit airplane scarves and loose clothes can get caught in the blades of the plane."

Mary Sharp covered her face, "Gruesome!"

"Yes, can you imagine it?" Evelyn stifled a snicker, narrowed her eyes, and deepened her voice, "The pilot's face turns red as the scarf tightens around her neck. Blood squirts out her eye sockets."

"Evelyn!"

Using her hands as props, her daughter continued. "The tightening scarf pulls the pilot over the plane's outer shell while her fingernails split as she claws at the plane's covering. Closer and closer, until the whirling propeller snatches her limbs." Evelyn's eyes enlarged, and her voice rasped, "Her body splatters. Legs and arms dangle off the propeller until she drops to her death."

"Good grief, Evelyn. What a horrible imagination."

Evelyn giggled, "It was wondrously gruesome." Sher grabbed her pen and circled the name of Thea Rasche, Europe's foremost aviatrix. "Mama, Rasche is the first German woman fly a U 12." She grabbed a scrapbook, "See here, Mama? I got a picture from National Geographic. She flies in an open cockpit, so she wears coveralls and a flight helmet."

Mary Sharp frowned and clicked her lips, "Tk-tsk. She wears men's clothes?"

"Well, of course," Evelyn crossed her arms, "how can she climb into an airplane wearing a dress?"

Her mother rolled her eyes and shook her head, "How lady-like." she mumbled.

Evelyn ignored her mother. "Rasche is favored by some sports' writers." Evelyn raised her eyebrows and grinned. "Of course, she's got to beat Amelia Earhart. Amelia's the sure bet."

On August 18, 1929, Evelyn's chin rested in one hand and elbow while her legs sprawled on the rag rug. Scrap books and pencils lay scattered around her. "I'm ready and waiting for action. I can't believe this is happening!" She squealed in a high-pitched voice, "The first U.S. Women's Air Derby transcontinental race!" Her father moved his chair close to the radio. "Turn it up, Papa, I want to hear the official race registration."

"Evelyn, calm down." Her mother called from the kitchen.

Evelyn rolled her eyes. "Papa, the pilots will fly from California to Ohio. The trip takes eight days of solo flying without any navigational instruments! That's hard, isn't it, Papa?"

"Sounds that way to me." He grinned at Evelyn's enthusiasm. Pointing to a map cut from the newspaper, Evelyn's finger traced the planned route, "They have fifteen planned stops for refueling and sleep." Her eyes enlarged. "The paper says the route and distance would challenge any aviator, man or woman."

"And" John waited for his daughter's reaction, "I read that male aviators think the women will run out of gas. You, know, not have the stamina to finish the distance."

Evelyn dropped her pencil and whipped her head around. "The female aviators like Amelia and Pancho are real aces and can't wait to prove their aeronautical abilities!" John slapped his knee and snorted at his daughter's defensive voice.

"Papa, the broadcaster said there is oily smell from the sun melting the tar runways." Evelyn's narrowed eyes darkened. "Will that cause problems for the take-offs?"

"This race has attracted world-wide attention. I bet when the organizers scheduled the starting point from the Santa Monica Airport - in sunny California during the hottest month of the year - they planned for any situation."

Evelyn cranked up the radio dial when the announcer described famous photographers and movie stars who strolled through the crowd. "Folks, Howard Hughes visited the female pilots and wished them luck. I am sure my listeners know that the Hughes Aircraft company produces the H-4 Hercules aircraft."

"Howard Hughes, the handsome millionaire!" Evelyn threw her arms into the air and her voice hit another high octave note, "Can you beat that? He's such a dreamboat."

Her startled father dropped his newspaper, "Great Scott, Evelyn!"

The broadcaster then called out to the American humorist, "Will Rogers! Oh Mr. Rogers, can I ask you a question?"

"Oh, oh." Evelyn frowned and leaned her ear closer. The day before, the American humorist Rogers remarked to a local newspaper that since the contestants were women, the aviation race should be named the 'power-puff derby.'

The female aviators concluded that the term 'power-puff' demeaned their abilities. The newspaper quoted Aviator Pancho

Barnes. "We don't want to be identified as females; we are qualified pilots."

The announcer continued, "The contestants are unhappy about your comments. How do you respond?"

"Aw, I was joking as usual," Rogers's voice cackled. "But they can prove themselves today."

Evelyn squinted her eyes. "He better watch what he says next time. Some woman is gonna knock his block off!"

"Evelyn!" her mother shouted from the kitchen. "Women don't hit other people."

Evelyn crossed her arms. "I would." Her father snickered behind his newspaper.

The announcer's voice crackled over the airwaves and supplied an eye's view of the pilots as they processed entry papers. "Fellow Americans, Louise Thaden came dressed in her usual black pants and black leather boots."

Evelyn clapped her hands and squealed, "I knew it! I knew she' dress in black." She rushed over to her father's chair, "Here's a photo from Life magazine, Papa."

"My, my," he shook his head and chuckled, "she looks dangerous." The broadcaster continued, "Making history in this first Women's Air Derby, Florence "Pancho" Lowe Barnes signs in next." The announcer's voice lowered, "Her real name is Florence Leontine Lowe. And for those who don't know," his voice whispered over the radio, "Pancho was raised in mansion in San Marino, California. Her famous grandfather is none other than Thaddeus S.C. Lowe's, the American aviation pioneer."

"Can you beat that!" Evelyn's mother wiped her hands on a tea towel. "She has all that money but still wants to fly airplanes."

"Mama, she loves adventure. Her grandpa took her to air shows when she was ten years old like me," Evelyn retorted. "You do remember, don't you? When I was little, I told you I'm going to fly airplanes someday."

Mary Sharp tipped her head sideways and frowned.

Evelyn jetted out her chin. "You wait and see!"

John Sharp approved of Evelyn's enthusiasm, but his smile faded as he remembered that American girls had few opportunities, especially for a young girl from small-town Nebraska.

"Listen, listen!" Evelyn placed her ear close to the speaker, "It's Pancho's voice."

"We pilots will show everybody. We can fly as darn fast and as far as any man." The crowds cheered, joined by Evelyn.

"Papa, the newspaper reported the race will cover 2,759 miles in nine days." Her father whistled, "What's the prize?"

"Eight thousand dollars!" Evelyn grinned and whispered, "That's a lot of money, huh?"

"Well, that's above my pay grade. More than I could make in five years of hard work."

"They're worth it." She studied her maps and rechecked her articles. "Fifteen planned stops from Santa Monica, California to Cleveland, Ohio."

"That's a lot of flying, daughter."

"They can do it, for sure!"

Sunday morning, August 18th, Evelyn sat in her pajamas next to the radio and ate her breakfast surrounded by her scrapbooks and the morning's newspaper. "Today, I going to add race details." When the newscaster reported that the air temperature at the airport was a sweltering 105 degrees," Evelyn recorded the fact in her journal.

Mary studied Evelyn's dedication, "Maybe you'll be a news reporter someday."

"Oh, Mama, stop teasing," she frowned and continued writing in her journals. "You know I'm going to be a pilot."

Mary hissed at her husband, "Stop encouraging her. You know she can't fly an airplane. Poor girls from Nebraska don't do such things."

John Sharp patted his wife's shoulder, "There's plenty of time for her to experience the unfair rules for girls. Let her have some fun."

The young girl didn't notice her parents' exchange. "I read the contestants shared maps, route ideas, and tips about the terrain yesterday." Evelyn glanced at her father and grinned, "That's what I call a team."

"Folks, you should see Amelia Earhart's plane," the radio blasted. "It's a red, five-passenger Lockheed Vega monoplane with Amelia Earhart in the enclosed cockpit." *Gee, I wish I could see that.* The radio blared. "Hold on to your seats, the pilots are headed to their planes for this history- making race!"

When the pilots started their engines and engaged the planes' propellers, the noise reverberated over hundreds of miles of radio waves and filled the Sharp home in Broken Bow, Nebraska. Evelyn clutched her pencil and recorded the times next to the names of the fourteen pilots competing in the heavy class and the six women flying in the lighter class. "The pilots arranged their planes in the order that they registered and will depart one after the other."

Evelyn emitted a long sigh. *Someday, I'm going to do that!*

Over the next nine days, Evelyn listened to the radio and read newspaper articles. Her best friend, Irene, helped record information about each designated stop including the finishing city, Cleveland. At each planned stop, the pilots stayed overnight, refueled their plane, and fixed any needed repairs. On day one, Evelyn and Irene wrote the time of arrival at the first layover in Yuma, Arizona. That evening, Evelyn listened to the pilots' publicity speeches. "Mama, the newspaper said the pilots hope their interviews help America accept professional female aviators."

"Well, I suppose there are people who will listen." Mary pursed her lips and scrunched her face.

"Of course," Evelyn frowned at Mary, "I know I will. I'm going to be a pilot like them." Mary drummed her fingers on the kitchen table and bit her lip but didn't argue with her daughter.

The planes landed on day two in Phoenix and Douglas, Arizona, Evelyn and Irene recorded the fliers' routines as the pilots headed their planes toward Texas. Day three brought the aviators to El Paso. On day four, the planes landed in Pecos, Texas. Day five ended when they reached Midland, Texas. The pilots whirled on to Abilene on day six and then to Fort Worth on the seventh day. Each evening Evelyn listened as the pilots spoke to the waiting crowds. The end of day eight found the pilots at their layover in St. Louis, Missouri. The prize waited two stops away.

"This is the last day of the race." Evelyn gobbled her scrambled eggs. "The planes head to Cincinnati, Ohio." Evelyn ran to the radio with her ear near the speaker.

"Evelyn, do something other than sit next to that radio. Help me by dusting the furniture," her frustrated mother of radio announcers blaring in her living room.

"After they take off, Mama. Then I will, that is until they land."

"Citizens of America, you wouldn't believe it. I estimate a crowd of eighteen thousand people waiting on the tarmac," the broadcaster's voice danced with excitement. "There is electricity in the air, dear friends. It's one heck of a greeting party!"

Boy, oh boy, I wish I could be there. Evelyn plopped in front of the family's radio. She gripped her pencil and her notebooks, ready to record all the details. As each plane landed, the radio listed the name of the pilot and her race statistics. Irene rushed through the front door and sat by Evelyn's side. "I had to wash the dishes before I could come." Irene rolled her eyes. "My mother is not keen on these women pilots."

"Well, tell her that Louise Thaden landed in Cleveland and claimed the first prize!"

Evelyn recorded Thaden's name in the heavy-weight class with a time of twenty hours, nineteen minutes, and four seconds and Irene added the figures into the charts. "I hoped Emelia would win," Evelyn pouted, "but Thaden is a good pilot too." Irene patted Evelyn's shoulder.

The radio crackled again, "Here comes the plane piloted by Phoebe Omlie! She wins the light-weight class in twenty-five hours, twelve minutes, and forty-seven seconds." Evelyn and Irene listed the detailed information in her tally book. The friends kept their heads together until all the pilots had landed. Mary Sharp joined her daughter and Irene and listened to the speeches. The pilots' triumphant endeavor was heard around the world.

American women and girls, especially Evelyn Sharp, revered their new heroes. A female champion had faced ridicule and contempt but defied gender limitations. No longer a dream, women

around the world would fly among the clouds. Evelyn Sharp
dreamed she would soar above all obstacles and become an aviator.

CHAPTER 2

Free to Dream

Evelyn's father, John Sharp, was a dreamer and a risk-taker who always searched for the next big opportunity. He and Mary ran two grocery stores in Montana before a fire resulted in the family's move to Hastings, Nebraska in 1924. There he and his wife owned and operated a grocery store. Customers engaged in conversation with the five-year- old who sat on the counter next to the cash register. But then the dreamer bought a cattle ranch in the Nebraska Sandhills and uprooted his family in March 1928. Evelyn rode her pony, Chalky, to the nearest country school and sold vegetables at a stand near Broken Bow. However, the harsh weather, sandy soil, and little rain made farming difficult. Less than three years later, the Sharps resettled in the small city of Ord tucked into the North Loup River valley on the east side of the Nebraska Sandhills.

With a population of three thousand, the town had businesses, churches, a grade school, and a high school. During the 1932 Depression when money was tight for Americans, the risk-taker leased the Old Ravenna Creamery building. It didn't matter that

John had no experience in the ice cream business. He renamed the shop, The Home Ice Cream Factory, and made two batches of ice cream daily. Each summer morning and then again in the afternoon, thirteen-year-old Evelyn rode her cart along the tree-lined streets of Ord and sold double-dip cones for a nickel.

"Okay, Papa. I'm headed to the south side of town today. Come on Perp, jump on up." Evelyn never left her house without Perp, a tiny black and white mutt. "Get a 'going, Chalky," she snapped the reins. As she and her companions moseyed down the street, she'd call out. "Ice cream! Ice cream cones, only five cents!"

Irene rode along on a few hot days. "Evelyn, don't you get hot and tired of driving around Ord all summer?"

"Gosh, no. I make new friends every day." She grinned and snapped the reins. "I will know all the names of the students in grade school by this fall." Not just young people enjoyed ice cream. Grown-ups strolled from their front porches. "Hey, Evelyn! What flavors do you have today?"

"Chocolate!"

"Ride on up and give me two cones. My wife will mad if I don't get one for her."

Everyone liked the taste of summer. By fall, Evelyn Sharp had met everyone in Ord.

Waiting for Evelyn at the kitchen door, Mary's shoe tapped on the floor. "I see you have on your usual pants." Before Evelyn would answer, her mother snapped. "Mr. Jones at the grocery asked me which sport my tomboy was playing today. I was mortified!"

"Oh, Mama, I like my reputation. It means I'm tough like the boys." When not in school, Evelyn dressed in overalls or old jeans anchored with suspenders, ready to join any neighborhood game.

Her mother plopped her hands on her hips. "We don't live on the ranch any longer, and you're not four years old. Stop wearing those overalls."

"But Mama, they're so comfortable. When I climb in and out of the ice cream cart, I don't want a dress blowing up in the air or getting caught in the wheels."

Mary Sharp couldn't disagree and let out a loud groan, "Well, put on a dress when you get home."

Evelyn nodded, but behind her back, she crossed her fingers. *When I race on the playground or play baseball in the park, dresses get in the way. No way does a dress help me win at game of kick-the-can, marbles, or box ball.*

Her father encouraged his daughter's athleticism. During the summers, he and his Evelyn fished in the North Loup River. During the autumn season, they hunted quail, pheasants, and turkeys. "Pheasant season starts tomorrow. Let's head out early." Season after season, John and Evelyn stalked the Nebraska grain fields and creek bottoms near Ord. By the time she was ten years old, Evelyn could use her shotgun and hit pheasants on the fly.

CHAPTER 3

Need to Be Physical!

During the Great Depression, 1933, Evelyn Sharp attended Ord high school's freshmen class and joined the Girls' Athletic Association - her second home. During summer, tennis matches filled her days. In the early days of autumn, she continued tennis after school. She'd rush home with her face and neck covered in sweat. Evelyn didn't mind, the exercise exhilarated her.

Mary picked up a tea towel and tossed it to her daughter. "Wipe that sweat off and brush the hair from your face. This is not how a young lady should look." Her mother's forehead furled. "Why do you go to this gym every day? Don't you want to come home after spending hours in classes?"

"To do what?" Evelyn cocked her head and grabbed an apple off the table. *What's up with Mama today?*

"You could talk to me." When Evelyn didn't answer, she added, "Or you could read a book? Something more feminine." Her mother crossed her arms.

"Oh, Mama, my body craves exercise. School's fun, but I'm trapped at a desk all day. My leg muscles twitch, and I need to run!"

"Auch! No talking to you, is there?" Mary stomped to her bedroom.

Evelyn shrugged her shoulders and finished her apple.

After the weather cooled, the gym organized volleyball matches indoors. Evelyn liked volleyball, but basketball was the sport she enjoyed the most. However, Evelyn's competitiveness created waves among the players and their parents. It was obvious that she and Irene were athletically talented. It was true that they dribbled and shot the ball better and more often than the other girls. Evidentially, the coach pulled the two friends aside after the game.

"Girls, I'm getting complaints from the other girls' parents. They say you two are grandstanding and not letting the others handle the ball."

"Gee Whiz! Who said that?" Their eyes widened in surprise. "I guess we do make a lot of points." Evelyn turned to her friend and shrugged her shoulders.

"And" the coach crossed his arms, "you can't always play on the offensive side of the court. We must allow the others a chance to score baskets."

"What? Good grief!" Irene raised her voice.

"Calm down, now." Her coach put her hand on Irene's shoulder. "Don't be a poor sport."

"Yeah, I know." Evelyn stepped closer to the coach. "But I don't understand why girls can't play full court basketball. It makes no sense. It's stupid that we have to stay on one side of the basketball court for defense then pass the ball to the other side for our team's offense." Her coach shrugged her shoulders. "I can dribble the ball down the full court and shoot the basketball just as well as any boy!"

"I told you, Evelyn," her coach groaned, "it's silly. I agree. But I don't have any power over the state school officials. They reckon girls lack stamina for the physical exertion of athletics."

"Well, that's plain stupid!" Evelyn Sharp put her hands on her hips and narrowed her eyes. "Put me into a basketball game with any of the boys, and I'll outlast them!"

"I don't doubt that you could. Then wait for angry remarks from the boys' parents." The coach laughed. "You'd run rings around the boys. But I don't make the rules." Her coach shrugged her shoulders and shook her head. "Maybe someday but not right now."

"Good grief, this isn't fair. Irene and I didn't realize we monopolized the basketball. But why do some old geezers in Lincoln get to decide if I'm tough enough to play full-court basketball?"

Her coach shook her head, "I agree. I'd love to play full court too. But that's the government, I guess."

Evelyn spun around and stomped out of the gym. When she entered her house, she let the screen door slam behind her. "Mama, the rules in sports are different for girls than for boys." Evelyn gulped a glass of lemonade.

Her mother raised her eyebrows and threw up her hands, "Rules always benefit men. It's the way of life."

Wrinkling her forehead, Evelyn frowned. "But why? Why do men get more chances? Why do men get to make the decisions?"

"I believe it has been that way since Adam took the apple from Eve and then blamed her for his choice."

Evelyn plopped her arms on the kitchen table, "I don't get it. Why don't women complain or something?"

"Oh, how we wish we could. Some have and of course lost." Mary sat down at the table and reached her hands out to her daughter, "It is a long-standing belief or unspoken rule. Women don't have the same chances as men." Mary's voice lowered, and she peered at Evelyn. "When I was young, I hoped to be a teacher. My parents didn't want money spent on a daughter. Anyway, I met your father and fell in love." Mary's smile was slim but tight.

Her daughter's mouth dropped open. Evelyn had no idea about her mother's dream. *I guess I don't know Mama very well.*

Mary squinted her eyes. "Did you know your female school-teachers aren't allowed to be married? Think about it, all your teachers were called Miss Something or Miss Whatever."

Evelyn's eyes widened. She figured that after they got married, teachers decided to stay home with their husbands. "Well, that's not fair. Why? What is getting married bad?"

"Fair or not, that is simply the way it is," Mary smirked. "You need to accept the fact that women do not have many opportunities."

"But I want to earn a letter in sports this year! Few girls do, and I really want to." Evelyn jumped from the table and ran to her mother. She wrapped her arms around frustrated Mary Sharp. "Mama, you were raised in a time when girls stayed in the house and learned to cook or sew. I want to do more."

"Okay, what is a letter in sports, and why do you want it?" Mary sighed.

"Students, boys or girls, join lots of sports like basketball and tennis and then earn points, see?" Evelyn's eyes sparkled, "If I get over 225 points, I get a patch with the letter "O" sewn on it. Because it stands for Ord High School, I can wear the patch on my school sweater."

Mary tipped her head, still confused.

"It's like a badge that proves I am good at sports." Evelyn twirled and danced around the room pretending to shoot basketballs into an imaginary hoop.

"Is being good at sports really so important?" Her mother didn't understand her daughter. "How will basketball and volleyball help you when you marry?"

"Oh, Mama, I love being competitive." Evelyn knelt next to her mother. "I can't sit still. I love pushing myself to be the best. It's like having a purpose in life. I try my best to reach my goal and have fun at same time. And Mama," Evelyn teased, "it keeps me busy and too tired to get into trouble. What do you think?"

"Well, that would be a good thing." Mary let out a long sigh.

With a huge grin, Evelyn added, "Plus, I need to be strong to climb into the cockpit of my airplane."

Mary's face flushed, and her eyes narrowed. "Evelyn, sit down a minute. We need to talk." Mary folded her arms. "I know your father supports your dreams, and dreams are good. But you are old enough to realize that dreams don't always come true."

Evelyn tilted her head. "Yeah, I know. Some don't."

Mary grabbed Evelyn's chin and glared into her daughter's eyes, "In America, not everyone thinks women should be so pushy and physical. Polite society does not like ambitious women." Evelyn blushed at her mother's criticism. "Women don't hold jobs like flying airplanes. Be honest, Evelyn. How many women pilots, do you know?"

Evelyn scratched her fingernail on the tablecloth. "Well, I guess not any." *What's Mama trying to tell me?*

"When I married your father, we owned a grocery in Montana. But he wanted to move, so I moved. I loved living in Hastings and running our grocery. But he thought he'd try farming. I followed him to the Sandhills." Mary wiped her eyes with her apron, "Now we are here in Ord and own an ice cream business without any past experience." She closed her eyes and nodded. "I pray each day that we stay in one place for a while."

Evelyn patted her mother's hand. "It was hard, wasn't it? I see that now."

"But, Evelyn, the point is that none of those decisions were my choices. I had no say." Evelyn studied her mother's calloused hands and tired eyes. *I never considered Mama's feelings. Papa should have asked Mama. Why didn't he?*

Mary pushed her chair back and rose from the table. She frowned down at her daughter, "I want you to enjoy your life now. But when you are older, you must accept the limitations of a woman's life."

Later Evelyn rode her bicycle to Irene's house. The two sat on the front step and talked about what happened with Evelyn's mother. "Mama is talking about back in her day, not now. We're the future. We're still going to play hard, Irene. They can't stop our enthusiasm."

"But I'll watch that I don't hog the ball." Irene hesitated. "You still look sad, what else is going on?"

While Evelyn shared more of her conversation with Mary Sharp, Irene studied the sidewalk and listened. "Well, this is the way I see it, Evelyn." Irene shrugged her shoulders, "After high school, I have no future plans. I don't dream about airplanes or soaring in the clouds. You are unusual."

Evelyn silently remembered their days in grade school. She didn't remember Irene talking about what she'd be when she grew up. "Well, what about being a nurse?"

Irene bumped her shoulder into Evelyn's. "Yeah, my parents don't have money to send me off to Omaha to a Nursing school. No, I'll get married and have a passel of kids." She grinned. "But that's okay. You are the one with dreams. I am fine with whatever fate gives me."

"Do you think I'm wrong in dreaming about flying?"

"Heck no! You dream and plan all you want. But remember your mother's advice. Some dreams don't come true. Just be prepared."

Evelyn shuffled home more confused than before. *Am I dreaming too big? I need a plan or just plain good luck.*

Mary Sharp didn't realize the magnitude of her daughter's determination. When Evelyn set a goal, she pushed with every fiber of her body. Failure didn't fit into her plans. The first major goal involved earning an athletic letter. As a student, she needed to be involved in the high school sports which were categorized as "Activities Under Supervision." The sports were: soccer, speedball, volleyball, basketball, or baseball. Each sport earned her 175 points each. In addition, she needed fifty more points from each "unsupervised" sport which included hiking, roller skating, bicycling, ice skating, golf, and tennis.

"See, Irene, I keep a daily tally, so I know exactly how many points I need by spring." Evelyn displayed her journal and pointed to the different columns she had created.

"I need to do that!" Irene Whiting and Evelyn practiced shooting baskets or played tennis for hours. The two friends pushed each other in school and sports.

However, the Nebraska Athletic Association had earlier issued a policy for high school girls' sports. The rules required that the focus of girls' sports should be on cooperation, sportsmanship, fun, and friendships. Competition was to be avoided. Just as Mary Sharp had once told her daughter, the public did not approve of pushy or physical girls. The focus of all female sports was camaraderie and teamwork.

In class one afternoon, Evelyn and Irene received a memo requesting them to meet with the principal after school hours. Evelyn's face turned red with embarrassment. She had never been sent to the principal's office. She turned and spotted Irene's face which had turned pale. Both girls shrugged their shoulders and tried to concentrate on geometry.

"What did we do wrong? Did you cheat or something?" At the end of class, Irene grabbed Evelyn's arm. "I've never been sent to the office."

"No, I didn't cheat. But maybe we're not in trouble. We might get some reward."

Irene stared at Evelyn's blank face, and then they both broke out in laughter. "Yeah, right. We're some kind of heroes."

The girls held hands when they stepped into Mr. Paxton's office but relaxed when he greeted them with a smile. "You're not in trouble, girls. I'd like to talk about girls' sports."

"Sure thing, Mr. Paxton." Evelyn and Irene were aware that they were the best female athletes in high school. *He knows what killer-diller athletes Irene and I are.*

"I'm sure you know already," he started with a quiet tone, "about the Nebraska Athletic Association's policy concerning girls' sporting competitions."

Stunned, Evelyn's voice quivered. "Yeah, but we're cooperating with teammates when making scores. We're friends with all the girls." Evelyn straightened her back but tried not to act defensively.

"Yes, I know. But I have received complaints." Mr. Paxton fiddled with a pen on his desk, then frowned at the girls. "But since you two always win each girls' competitions, some parents believe that you should let the other girls have more chances."

The girls gawked surprised. "Parents think we play unfairly? That's a bum rap." Evelyn's face flushed.

"I am sorry, girls. I love sports myself." Paxton rose from his chair, rounded the desk, and sat facing the students. "But this policy dictates that girl athletes must focus on cooperation. Our coaches are compelled to follow those rules. I know your basketball coach has already spoken with you both. Competition and the goal of winning should be frowned upon."

"Good grief, Mr. Paxton." Evelyn's face flushed red with anger. "That's simply not fair. Boys try their best!"

"Yes, that's true. But boys are expected to be tough and learn to defend themselves. It prepares them to protect their families one day."

"Mr. Paxton, I respect you, I do." Evelyn clenched her jaw. "But you know that is a cheesy reason, don't you?" Paxton frowned but remained silent.

Irene crossed her arms. "Besides, we don't push anyone or hurt them. If they don't want to play competitive, then they don't have to be involved."

Mr. Paxton chuckled. "Well, girls, you made a good argument. But as principal, I must follow the state rules. That is all there is to it." He ushered Evelyn and Irene out from his office but then added. "Continue striving and gaining skills. But girls, gauge how hard you push your teammates during competitions."

The best friends strolled to the athletic association in slow motion. "I can't believe this. People complain because we win?" Evelyn shook her head. "I wonder who complained."

Irene glanced at the other students heading to the gym. "I can guess."

"Don't say any names, but I have suspicions too. I can't think about it too much, or I won't be able to be nice to them. I don't want that."

"You're right. But I don't care about silly rules." The friends stopped and shook hands.

"Now you're cooking with gas. We still compete, but not so obviously." Evelyn slapped her friend on her back, and they headed off to play basketball. Evelyn and Irene cooperated and shared sporting opportunities. They heartily encouraged their teammates and their opponents. But they still tried to win! At the Spring Sports Banquet, Evelyn and Irene were the two freshmen girls to earn a sports' letter. The friends concealed their pride until they headed for home with their parents.

"Evelyn, you made me proud," John beamed. Evelyn and Irene winked at each other. "Having fun, Papa. Simply having fun."

But the school and the gym were not the exclusive places which offered Evelyn opportunities. In every activity such as the local Ord Campfire Girls Troop, chorus, drama, or band, Evelyn Sharp aspired for par excellence. It was her nature. She yearned to do the best job in every commitment. There was no public swimming pool in Ord. But that didn't stop people from enjoying hot days.

Adults, children, and young friends joined on the banks of the North Loup River. The small town of Ord, in the middle of Nebraska, offered Evelyn Sharp a place to thrive and flourish. Her future – like the sky – was limitless.

CHAPTER 4

Living a
Double Life

After a few years, John Sharp started a restaurant which also offered sleeping rooms in the back of the building. During the Great Depression, traveling salesmen or itinerary workers needed to rent rooms while on jobs in Ord. One of those workers was Jack Jefford, a pilot. Jefford and his brother grew up on a ranch in McGrew, Nebraska which was approximately three hundred miles away. In addition to ranching, the two brothers had established the Jeffords' Aviation Services in Broken Bow, a town fifty miles west of Ord. The brothers owned a plane that was called the D-1 Fly About which had a side-by-side, two-seat cabin. Using their Fly About, the Jeffords started a second business in Ord and offered flying lessons.

Town's people daily observed the airplane flying in the clouds above, over the town, and from the airfield. In John Sharp's café, the morning coffee hour enjoyed lively conversations. "Boy, oh boy, I wish I had some money, I'd be first in line to learn to fly." Sixty-year-old Elmer Hansen stirred sugar into his coffee.

"I don't know anyone who has enough money for such a thing." His neighbor Harvey Claussen leaned back in his wooden chair and winked at the other men sitting around their table.

Eighty-year-old, Carson Fleming slapped the top of the table and shouted, "Hot diggity-dog! If I had me some money, I'd fly up to the sky and walk on one of those airplane wings!"

Sharp's patrons at the café could talk of nothing else other than Jack Jefford's flying business. "Yeah, but have you heard of anyone taking lessons?" Tom Johnson threaded his thumbs under his suspenders and narrowed his eyes. "So, if people aren't waiting in line for lessons, I don't figure he'll stay long." But fate – just as fickle as the Nebraska weather – stepped in and changed the world for Jack Jefford and Evelyn Sharp.

To save time and money Jack Jefford had been renting one of the sleeping rooms in the back of John Sharp's restaurant. After three months, Jack had just two flying students. Since not enough money was coming in, he and his brother considered closing the flight school. He arranged a meeting with Sharp at the café. "Mr. Sharp, I don't have enough money to pay my past-due bill." Jack blushed in embarrassment. "I don't teach enough students."

"Well, Jack, I've been thinking about your debt." John Sharp – looking for a new opportunity as usual – pulled out a chair and motioned for Jack to do the same. "I've got a proposition for you." Sharp paused and drummed his fingers on the tablecloth while Jack cocked his head with curiosity. "My daughter, Evelyn, has been talking about learning to fly since a little girl."

Jack leaned closer to the table and nodded. "Yeah, I see." Math calculations danced in his head.

"I don't have any extra cash for lessons," John Sharp stared at Jefford, "but we might reach a mutually beneficial arrangement about my rent and your time." He leaned back in the chair and scrutinized Jefford's reaction. Sharp imagined Jefford's mind calculating his costs and expenses.

"I'll do it. I'll teach Evelyn weekly and take the costs for lessons out in trade for my bill! That's what you were thinking. Right?"

Sharp cackled and reached his hand over the checkered tablecloth. "Let's shake." Jack let out a loud sigh of relief. But the two men's satisfaction couldn't match Evelyn's jubilance. From the corner of the café's kitchen, she had overheard the agreement. She covered her mouth and silently bounced up and down. Not wanting to be discovered, she turned and raced the stairs two steps at a time. Evelyn Sharp jumped onto her bed, buried her head in her feather pillow, and muffled her screams of joy!

The next morning, Evelyn was up and dressed early. She ran over the Irene's house. When Irene opened the kitchen door, Evelyn screamed and scared her friend almost to death. "I'm going to learn how to fly!"

On February 4, 1935, Evelyn Sharp fought against the brisk winter wind and raced across the tarmac towards Jefford's plane. Jack grinned and watched the pleasure dance on the fifteen-year-old's face. He helped Evelyn climb up on the wing struts and then through the small door.

"Evelyn stepped in and slid down into the passenger's seat, "Man, this is smaller than I figured. Will we fit?"

Jack roared. "Hey, rookie, what did you expect? This Fly About appears small, but it has power. You wait and see."

Positioned next to each other in the two aviator seats, Jack and Evelyn's shoulders touched. But Evelyn was too busy staring at the knobs and gauges to worry about being so close. Two large, iron steering wheels reached out toward the pilots' chest while their legs stretched toward two pedals in front of the seats. Jefford pointed down. "Evelyn, this plane has no brakes."

Her head spun toward Jack, and her jaw dropped. "What? How do you stop?"

"You'll learned about that later, but those pedals operate the rudders which control the plane's side-to-side movements. Don't step down or push unless you really want to fly sideways."

Evelyn stared ahead at the cockpit panel spread out from one side of the plane to the other. All sizes of labeled dials and gadgets faced the pilots in a random arrangement. "Guess I'll have to study these gauges a bit."

"You bet you will. These dials and gauges are lined up in a particular order of importance. Pilots don't have time to search for the right gauge. In the wink of an eye, a pilot needs to determine the plane's speed, altitude, sharpness of a climb or descent, and lastly, and whether or not to bank or turn. The order of the gauges needs to be memorized for quick and accurate access."

Evelyn placed her hand on the throttle positioned between the seats. *I am one of a few females in America who will learn to fly an airplane.* "Mr. Jefford, I understand how serious and dangerous aviation is. I promise, cross my heart, and hope to die, that I will use all my abilities to master this privilege." That first day, Evelyn rode in the seat beside Jack Jefford and scrutinized his actions. She studied the deliberate pressure and speed he used on the throttle and rudders. His seriousness and concentration proved his respect for the risks of aviation.

Later in her bedroom, Evelyn started a new journal. She labeled it "Flying in the Clouds." She also created a chart which listed her instructor's name and the type of aircraft – the D1 Fly About. In the future, she recorded the length of time for each flight, and the gauges she had used. Each night before she turned out her light, she analyzed the plane's manual and memorized the uses of the different gauges. Evelyn Sharp was determined that someday she would fly solo.

Evelyn Sharp, small town girl from Nebraska, lived a double life. During the day, the sophomore at Ord High School excelled in volleyball during the fall and dominated girls' basketball in the winter. She took part in all school activities, especially Ord's Girls' Glee Club. With the rest of her friends, including Irene, she played the piano and sang in music contests. Walking down the school halls, Evelyn was simply another teenaged girl dressed in puff-sleeved blouses and big skirts.

Wearing black and white saddle shoes and stylish argyle socks, she and her girlfriends talked about grades and boyfriends. "Did Bob Smith wink at you, Irene? Bet he has a crush on you."

Irene shoved her so hard, Evelyn flew across the hallway, bounced off two students, and almost careened into the lockers. A strong arm caught her just in time. "Oh, hi, Tom." Evelyn stuttered and tried not to blush. "Thanks for saving me."

"Any time, Evelyn." He winked and headed to his class.

Her other life began after 3:30 pm. Like Superman, Evelyn Sharp changed her school clothes and dressed in slacks, a sweater, and overcoat. Then she sauntered out toward the Ord airfield. No longer a small-town student, she had transformed into a serious air flight student who practiced takeoffs and landings.

But the real world still existed. The extended drought in the middle of America raised dust into the air and cancelled days of flying lessons. On April 14, 1935 – eventually labeled Black Sunday – dust storms ravaged over six states including Nebraska. Sand dunes escaped the dried Sandhills' grasses and blew into the air like flying gunshots that ripped at the skin. The dried soil broke down into soft dust and created black clouds and shadows over the earth below. "This weather situation is bad." John shook his head at the Sharp family supper table. "When the farmers don't make money, businesses like ours don't make money. We'll have to work harder and see what happens."

Evelyn's food stuck in her mouth. "Papa, could this weather cause Jefford to close his flying business? I'll die if I don't have more flying lessons."

"Don't know, daughter. But the whole country's economy is hurting pretty bad."

"Evelyn!" her mother snapped. "People all over America are losing their jobs and their homes. You shouldn't be selfish about flying lessons."

Evelyn nodded but silently prayed that Jack Jefford's business would continue.

CHAPTER 5

Dust and Fame

The following May, Evelyn and Irene Whiting finished their sophomore year and earned another letter in athletics. Before the school Prom, Evelyn began dating a boy in the junior class who worked at the airport. "Tom's a dreamboat. You sure are lucky." The girls teased Evelyn in the girls' locker room. "What does he think about all that time you spend in that airplane with another man?"

"Tom works at the airport, remember? He likes Jack Jefford. You worry about your boyfriend, and I will focus on mine." Evelyn flashed the girls a grin and sauntered away. *I can't worry about what others think. I have plans for my future.*

When not in the cockpit of an airplane, Evelyn continued her life as a young girl in small-town Nebraska. Teens, especially girls, didn't have much freedom. In the 1930s, a proper, young lady was not to be forward or bold. She wasn't to speak loudly in public or tell jokes. Evelyn had already broken some of those rules. Finally, Mary had complained enough so Evelyn stopped wearing her overalls during the summer. But now, as teenager, she wore long cotton trousers during flying lessons. Everyone knew, but it didn't affect her popularity.

Parents and Ord High School organized monthly dances that were held in the school gym. Of course, parents and teachers lingered on the sidelines as chaperones. School dances were one of the few chances to see friends other than in the classroom. But girls couldn't just show up at the dance. Boys were expected to ask a girl out and then pick her up in his parents' car. Most young people learned to dance, or they had to sit on the sidelines. Evelyn, Tom, and her friends danced the swing, foxtrot, and jitterbug. Tom and Evelyn had a standing date on Saturday night and attended the movies at the Golden Husk in downtown Ord. The theater was large enough to hold five hundred patrons. Tom's favorite movie was *My Man Godfrey.* Evelyn loved the song and dance movies like *Swing Time.*

One evening close to the end of May 1935, Evelyn once again wrote in her journal. She had flown six hours in three different types of aircraft with two different instructors. *I hope my dream never dies. Flying is accelerating, but I am anxious about learning to stall the engine.*

"Alright, Evelyn, next you'll learn to make figure-eight in the air. This exercise improves your coordination and smooth control when completing the pattern. After several practices, Evelyn performed the figure eight perfectly. The next lesson was the stall. "This maneuver is designed to detect if there is a problem with the airflow over the wings. This technique teaches pilots to acquire an automatic reaction when a problem occurs. Then they needed to be able to engage a system of recovery procedures."

"I'm glad Mama and Papa aren't out here. I'm sure Mama would faint."

During the procedure, Evelyn flew the plane upward at an angle of attack and increased the speed beyond a certain point where 'lift' stopped so the plane couldn't go higher. The engine stalled or stopped operating. After it turned back toward earth, Evelyn re-engaged the engine and regained control of the plane. *I did it! I'm closer to that pilot's license.*

"Evelyn, do you ever get tired from running here and there? You don't have any time left at the end of the day." Irene sat next to her best friend at lunch. "I don't get to see you anymore. You are either in class, at the gym practicing basketball, or running out to the airport."

"No, I love it." Evelyn then noticed the pout on Irene's face. "Hey, summer's coming. We'll have lot of time for fun." Summers were the young woman's favorite time of the year. Friends, especially Irene, appreciated Evelyn's love of excitement. Even though her boyfriend supported her dream of flying, he convinced Evelyn to save Friday nights for driving in the car down main street and Saturday nights for the movies for him.

During the warm months, the young people of Ord headed out to the North Loup River. Formed by a natural spring, cold, clear water bubbled up from the Sandhills' aquafer miles below. The sparkling river water trickled over a sandy bottom. There were areas of hazardous deep, swirling water, so Evelyn and her friends were trained as lifeguards. They also used the shallow areas and sand bars for teaching swimming lessons to Ord's children. In the cool of the evenings, Evelyn joined the swimming parties and bonfires and hung out with Tom and friends at the drive-in movies.

Taking advantage of the summer weather, Evelyn practiced flying as much as she could without abandoning her friends. Flying was her top priority. Since Evelyn lacked a pilot's license, especially one authorizing night flying, any aviation lessons needed to be completed by sundown. Summer days were longer and allowed more time in the air.

After conducting the stall maneuvers, Evelyn moved on to the difficult and dangerous technique called the tailspin. "You have to learn this skill because it is a mandatory requirement for obtaining a pilot's license." Evelyn needed no further encouragement. The complex maneuver could not have any errors. Distractions or mistakes could cause a plane crash or cost Evelyn her life. During the tailspin procedure, a pilot first performs a stall which Evelyn had already done. But the next step involved dropping one wing downward at the beginning of the stall. This action put the airplane into a spinning pattern toward the ground.

Trusting her abilities, Evelyn's brain fought off any panic. After the stall and during the tailspin, Evelyn then kept the necessary speed of fifty-five kilometers. The plane spun downward until Evelyn pulled the nose up and flattened the airplane out of the spin. *I'm on my way toward getting a license!*

During the next months, Evelyn trained for the last major technique a short field landing which took courage. "Ever since the first day that you climbed onto my plane, you have surprised me with your diligence and attitude for aviation. But, Evelyn, now you need nerves of steel." Jack put his hands on her shoulders and stared at his pupil. "Pilots use this skill when the landing area is too short or when the wings might hit an object too close to the landing strip." Evelyn nodded, and he continued. "You are going to ease the plane down onto a soft area and minimize any chance of the surface grabbing a wheel." Jefford focused on Evelyn's eyes. "You managed the tailspin perfectly. You should be able to do this too. But there can be no errors. You listen to your head, not your gut."

The student practiced drifting the plane down as close to the end of the runway as possible. Evelyn then used a skid maneuver which involved dragging the tail of the plane or skidding until friction stopped the plane. *Boy, Jack was right. My heart is pounding, and my hands are trembling.* "You're going great. Keep breathing." Jack sat next to his pupil and coaxed her courage. Day after day, she and Jack flew off into the sky and then Evelyn practiced short landings. Once she practiced by easing the plane down into a harvested, corn field. Cornhusks flew into the air as the plane's tail dragged along the rows of corn stalks. The next day, Jefford told Evelyn that she would land the plane on the frozen North Loup River.

"Okay, Mr. Jefford. But that river better be frozen three feet deep!" Evelyn loved the exhilaration of aviation. The intense concentration needed while reading the cockpit panel gauges invigorated her mind. Each time her plane lifted off the runway and again when she landed, her heart pounded. Quitting was never a choice.

During the fall months of her junior year in high school, volleyball matches, and music contests kept her days busy. Her mother didn't discourage her daughter from her flying lessons as long as Evelyn's grades were good. The young woman confidently managed her two worlds and continued with her combined life of high school activities and flying.

December and January revved up the winter weather assault on the Nebraska landscape with blinding blizzards and icy runways. Pilots then changed their flying methods. Without cockpit heat, freezing temperatures and the added wind chill of the high altitudes changed flying into a formidable task. Most male pilots wore cotton overalls with added overcoats. Some pilots accessed leather jackets with extra padding on the collars which wrapped around their necks during flights. Of course, a small-town girl could not afford such outfits.

Late one afternoon, Evelyn pounded the snow off her shoes and entered the kitchen with chattering teeth. Mary Sharp raced across the room and placed her palms on Evelyn's cheeks. "Those white patches on your cheeks signal frost bite!" Mary pulled off Evelyn's mittens and squealed. "Your hands and fingers are frozen too. John, get in here quick! Evelyn's skin needs immediate help."

John threw his newspaper to the floor and rushed into the kitchen. One look at the red and white blotches on Evelyn's face brought tears to his eyes. "Oh, Evelyn, you have to stop flying in this weather. You're going to get sick."

"No." Evelyn mumbled through her numb lips. "No!" The Sharps slowly submerged their daughter's hands into a basin of water, not hot or cold. "Ow, that hurts, Mama."

"Your hands and fingers are gonna sting until they thaw. You will have to get through it." Mary had learned about frostbite in Montana. The mother had to be tough to save her daughter's fingers. Mary glared at her husband, "See? This is what happens when you encourage Evelyn to do crazy things like flying airplanes in the winter. If she gets sick, it will be your fault."

"Mama, please don't blame Papa." While Evelyn's extremities thawed, John heated water for a warm bath.

"To keep you from getting a temperature, you must soak in Epson salt and warm water. Then Evelyn, we will talk about what we can do so that you can continue flying during the winter."

"Papa, please. I love flying. Talk to Mama."

Although Mary didn't agree with Evelyn's flying, she loved her daughter and would do anything for her. The following week, Mary – a talented seamstress – scrutinized pictures of Amelia Earhart and other female pilots. She studied Evelyn's posters of Louise Thaden's black pants and black leather boots as well as magazine photos of Pancho Barnes. Within a week's time, she had sewn a pair of coveralls for Evelyn and lined them with flannel. Mary spoke with her friends and borrowed a warm, man's wool coat. By the following week, Evelyn stood in the kitchen dressed in her new overalls. Around her neck, she wrapped a thick scarf knitted by her mother. "Mama, these are perfect. The cold won't bite me now!" The Sharps saved their money and by the end of the month, they bought leather boots for Evelyn and gloves lined with rabbit fur.

During 1936, lessons focused on flying a new aircraft. The Aeronca C-3 was known as the Flying Bathtub because pilots sat low in the cockpit. This lower seating made flight training less difficult. Designed with two seats and a thirty-six horse-powered engine, Evelyn continued perfecting her technique drills and practiced the different landings. She wrote in her flying journal that she was ready for a solo flight and hoped Jefford thought so too. On March 4, 1936, when Jefford and Evelyn pulled the plane to a stop on the runway, Jack jumped out of the Aeronca C-3 and down onto the tarmac. Evelyn gawked down at her instructor. *What's up?*

"Well, rookie, it's time to solo!"

Evelyn's mouth dropped open in surprise but then grinned and displayed a 'thumbs up.' She gripped the throttle, eased it back, and headed down the runway. *This is it!* Her heart pounded, and she experienced shortness of breath. She realized that because her knees trembled, her feet popped off the rudders. *Stop it! You have done this lots and lots of time. Now it's your time to prove that women can fly!*

With a last thrust of the throttle, the plane lifted off the tarmac and ascended into the wind. *You're flying solo.* Evelyn gazed down at the earth as a rush of adrenaline spread over her body. A giggle – infectious and uncontrollable – started low then grew louder. She didn't care if it sounded high-pitched or girlish, the thrill filled her mind and her soul. *All my wishes – all my dreams – have come true.* The young aviator circled the field several times then made a perfect three-point landing.

News of a high school girl flying solo soon reached local newspapers and then spread on the *Omaha World Herald*. The paper's wide readership in Nebraska and beyond reached national magazines as well as teletypes. Within weeks, photographers descended on the Ord airport and waited to interview Evelyn. The brisk, spring wind blew through her hair while she took a deep breath. Evelyn didn't know if she liked this new attention. *Oh, well, here I go.* The mob of reporters and photographers surrounded the teen aviator, pushed each other, and shouted questions.

One reporter shouted out. "Hey, young lady, didn't anyone tell you girls aren't supposed to fly?"

Evelyn grinned at the reporters and shook her head. "Nope. My papa and I knew I would."

A second reporter shouted out. "What will you do when you become famous?"

Evelyn's smile faded. She frowned at the group, titled her head, and considered her answer. "I don't want to be famous."

"Then why do it?" There was a pause while the reporters waited.

"I have always dreamed of flying an airplane. It doesn't matter if I am a girl; I loved it."

CHAPTER 6

Exciting Opportunities

After her junior year of high school ended, Evelyn placed her third letter "O" on her dresser and studied her image in the mirror. Her brown hair had grown to her shoulders, and she had lost her childhood freckles. *Sure, I can fly an airplane, but I am still the same person as before.* However, the coming summer months would differ from the year before. Flying drills and practices took more of her time so she didn't help with the Campfire Troop or teach swimming lessons.

"You're always at the airfield." Irene complained. "It's summer, can't you have fun too? This may be the last summer before our friends graduate next year and leave Ord."

Evelyn hugged her best friend. "You're right. I'll try."

"I know you love flying. But you still need friends, right?" Irene wondered if she should continue, but she did anyway. "And, Evelyn, do you really believe that there is still a future in aviation? Here in Nebraska? Where?"

Evelyn stared ahead but didn't answer. *I don't know.* "I don't worry about the future right now. I'm just having fun."

Tom didn't want to spend his last summer in Ord without his best girl. They watched local baseball games and attended summer parties. "I'm off to the university next fall. What do you think will happen to us?" Evelyn shrugged and wiped tears from her eyes. Tom and Evelyn continued dating until the fall after Tom's graduation Then college took Tom to the University of Nebraska in Lincoln where he studied architecture. Evelyn missed their friendship. There were always holidays and college breaks. But they both understood that she desired to become a pilot, and he needed more education.

Flying was now the top priority in Evelyn Sharp's life, and her passion fulfilled her spirit.

On June 3, 1936, Evelyn and her flight instructor flew in the Aeronca C-3 to Lincoln, Nebraska. She had logged twenty-six hours in the air which was one hour more than the least amount needed for obtaining her Amateur License. At age seventeen, Evelyn Sharp became Nebraska's youngest pilot. The small-town girl did not realize that Americans considered her dreams and opportunities unusual. Before the 1940s, a mere one-fourth of America's women earned their own money. A wife depended on a husband for her shelter and livelihood. Women who worked as full-time clerical staff earned less than $1,000 a year. Her mother once warned Evelyn about the limited future for women in America.

However, Evelyn Sharp remained a dreamer. But now she needed more than dreams. She needed cash. The cost of a pilot's license ranged between $500 and $750 – a great deal of money during the Depression years. Evelyn realized that she would need to be as determined as her hero, Amelia Earhart

In January 1937, Evelyn opened an envelope posted from Omaha, Nebraska. "I am afraid to look," she peeked up at her mother. Her fingers trembled as she pulled out the official-looking letter. Her mother jumped back when her daughter screamed and danced around the kitchen. "Papa, look what I got!" Evelyn rushed into the living room. "It's an invitation from Belle Hetzel." Mary and John Sharp glanced at each other confused.

"She's the Omaha South High School aviation teacher." Evelyn shared the letter. "She's invited me to a meeting at the Fontenelle Hotel." Evelyn whispered, "Where's is that, Papa? Far away?" The letter explained Hetzel planned to organize an area chapter of the Ninety-Nines Club, a club of women aviators. Amelia Earhart, the organization's first president, would be in attendance. Hetzel invited Evelyn to attend the dinner, business meeting, and then join the group. "Invite me! I can meet Amelia Earhart!" Evelyn grew quiet and her face turned ash-white. "Why would she invite me?"

John Sharp glanced up from the letter. "She must read those magazine articles."

"Can I go, Papa? Should I go? Am I too young?" Evelyn remembered that Omaha, the largest city in Nebraska, sat on the Missouri River over one-hundred and eighty miles away from Ord. "How can I go? Of course, I guess I could fly."

Unsure what this organization involved and the requirement of the members, John Sharp decided he would go along and learn about this chapter of the Ninety-Nines. When the day approached, the January skies of Nebraska were socked in with severe weather. Evelyn had not yet earned her instrumental license. If the ground wasn't visible, Evelyn Sharp could not fly.

"Don't cry, Evelyn. I think I have a plan." John's smile was thin and sly. "I visited the gas station and asked if any trucker drivers were headed for Omaha tomorrow."

Evelyn lifted her tear-streaked face. "What? Really?"

He nodded as his lips spread into a smile. "One local trucker agreed to let us ride along. But it will take over six hours of traveling so we leave early tomorrow morning." John Sharp's daughter dashed to his side and wrapped her arms around his neck. Her mother wiped tears with the corner of her apron.

In the dark and cold of a winter morning, the Sharps jumped up into the cab of a truck hauling cattle to the stockyard. *Oh, please don't let me smell like cows.* The trucker dropped them off at the stockyards on the south side of Omaha. John Sharp flagged down a taxicab which transported them to the Hotel Fontenelle at 1806 Douglas Street in downtown Omaha. Evelyn's mouth gapped open when they arrived at the hotel's front doors. The building, built in 1915, boasted of three hundred and fifty rooms. When they entered the lobby, both John and Evelyn gawked at the English-styled, Mahoney paneling and marble floors. Hotel guests who moved about the lobby were dressed in expensive clothing, and the clerks and bellhops wore matching outfits. "Oh, Papa, we don't belong here." Evelyn whispered.

"We're here now. This can't be any more frightening than pulling out of a spiraling maneuver." Evelyn giggled. The two Ord citizens approached the front desk, displayed Evelyn's invitation, and explained their story. A smiling hotel clerk led them to the lavatories and supplied soap and towels. Once the father and daughter had changed their clothes, they found the scheduled meeting in the ballroom. They stopped outside the door and gathered their courage.

"Papa, my knees are shaking so much. I don't know if I can breathe."

"This is your chance, daughter. Take it," John Sharp grinned down at Evelyn and imagined how her life would never be the same. On the evening of January 30, 1937, Evelyn Sharp entered the ballroom doors and was greeted by Belle Hetzel and Amelia Earhart.

"Welcome Evelyn." Belle Hetzel reached out her hand, "I have been waiting to meet Nebraska's youngest pilot. Well done." Evelyn's face flushed with emotion and wondered if she should pinch herself. Standing next to Belle, Amelia Earhart nodded at Evelyn and displayed her toothy grin. *She looks like her photos - freckles and red hair.*

Amelia Earhart continued. "Evelyn, I'm a small-town girl from Kansas. If I can make history, so can you."

Hetzel leaned near Evelyn and teased Earhart. "It's in her blood. Did you know her mother, Amy, was the first woman to climb Pikes Peak in Colorado?" Evelyn's eyes widened.

Earhart nodded back and chuckled. "But Evelyn, you wouldn't be here if you weren't destined to be a trail blazer too."

John waited off to the side and beamed at his daughter and her new, famous friends. During the meal and following meeting, Evelyn and John Sharp learned that the organization had been founded on November 2, 1929, at Curtiss Field in Valley Stream, Long Island, New York. That day, over 117 female pilots met for mutual support but also for business. The women aviators agreed that a central office be created for the safekeeping of exact files recording the accomplishments made by female pilots. Later in 1931, the members elected Amelia Earhart as the first president and chose the name *Ninety-Nines* representing the first ninety-nine charter members. The club then opened their membership to any women as soon as she became a licensed pilot. That night, women pilots like Jacqueline Cochran and Nancy Love introduced themselves and shared aviation stories. Evelyn was now more than a fan of these aviators; she would be a friend and teammate.

Another trucker gave the Sharps a ride to Ord that night. Evelyn turned to her father, "Papa, I can't believe I am the youngest female pilot in Nebraska."

"Well, daughter, you are. When your application was accepted tonight, you became a member of America's only female pilots' organization, the *Ninety-Nines*. Who would have guessed?"

"Papa," Evelyn stared up into the night sky, "I feel like I'm living in a dream. I am the luckiest girl ever."

During the following months, Evelyn enjoyed her senior year in high school by continuing her life as a student, singing in music contests, acting in the one-act play, and taking part in the school band. In the spring, Evelyn and her girlfriends dressed in their prom gowns. Tom returned to Ord and escorted Evelyn. May 28, 1937, Evelyn Sharp graduated. To no one's surprise, Evelyn accepted an award for the school's most athletic girl.

All the while, Evelyn added hours of flying until a tragedy occurred. One of Jefford's planes crashed and killed a student pilot. He closed his operation at Broken Bow and became the manager of the Hastings airport. The Great Depression made renting an airplane exceedingly difficult. Airplanes at different airports were busy transporting supplies or being used for crop dusting. Of course, Evelyn had no money, and John Sharp recognized that he would never be wealthy enough to buy Evelyn an airplane. But his mind continued planning.

Eventually, he created a plan. John met with Dr. Auble, a prominent businessman. As they talked about prospects and plans for Ord's growth, John Sharp wondered out loud, "Do think Evelyn's flying could add to the town's recognition? She could give rides at county fairs and pull banners advertising Ord."

"Hey, that's an innovative idea!"

Since 1926, barnstorming had captured the hearts of Midwest communities. Pilots who returned home from World War I flew around the countryside and stopped at county fairs or other celebrations. The barnstormers performed trick flying maneuvers like loop-to-loops or aeronautical stunts. Dr. Auble and John Sharp discovered that rural citizens streamed to local towns to watch the flying sensations. After the men drew up preliminary plans, Dr. Auble grinned. "I'll take these ideas to other businessmen here in town. This could be a boom for Ord." A few days later, Dr. Auble and other prominent men met with Evelyn and her father.

As the men stared at the young girl, Auble leaned ahead in his chair. "Evelyn, we are impressed with your arduous work in school, sports, and now flying. We think your aviation skills could be used to promote Ord." Evelyn's heart began beating fast in her chest. *What? What do they mean?* Her father had not shared the intent of the meeting. "So young lady, the businessmen here have agreed to put a down-payment on an airplane."

Evelyn's eyes stared wide. She gawked speechless and turned to her father. "Papa, what's going on?"

"Daughter, these men want to invest in your flying abilities. You will be a barnstormer for Ord."

Slowly, the idea of flying to county fairs and other towns made sense. "Oh, sir, thank you." Evelyn giggled with surprise. But then in a serious tone, she turned to the businessmen, "I will promote Ord with my whole heart."

"But" Dr. Auble spoke again, "there is one condition." Evelyn froze. "Since this is a major investment for a small town during the Depression, our condition is that you make the further payments." Evelyn stared while her brain whirled. *How can I earn money?* The investors guessed her concerns. "We suggest you do personal appearances and offer rides like other pilots in the Midwest. For a fee, of course. Some pilots have a dog ride along. I hear the crowds love it." Evelyn grinned and nodded as her brain filled with ideas. *I am on my way to having my own plane!*

CHAPTER 7

Living in the Clouds

August of 1937, Jack Jefford, Evelyn, and her father drove to Omaha. "Stop moving and fiddling in your seat." John turned to the backseat, "You're making me nervous too."

"I can't. How much farther?"

"The airport is on the northeast side of Omaha, Evelyn." Jefford glanced into the rearview mirror. "We have to drive through downtown and then to the north." As the car approached the airport tarmac and neared the airplane, the three occupants silently stared.

"Oh, it is beautiful!" Evelyn whispered. "I can't believe this is mine." Parked on the tarmac sat a Taylor Cub NC 19532 airplane. In 1931, Clarence Gilbert Taylor – referred to as the father of private aviation in America – had designed the original Taylor Cub in Bradford, Pennsylvania. The aircraft had wings mounted high on the fuselage and an open cockpit. The plane was powered by a twenty horsepower, Brownback Tiger Kitten, engine. Taylor chose to call his new airplane The Cub. This inventive plane had been flown from Pennsylvania to Omaha and waited for Evelyn and the city of Ord.

Evelyn strolled around the tubular steel body of the plane. Her fingertips moved along the wrapped fabric-covering of the body and then caressed the wings covered with airfoil. Evelyn Sharp suddenly declared, "This will be named The Ord."

Seventeen-year-old Evelyn Sharp was now one of seven other women in Nebraska who were plane owners. She started fulfilling her promise to the people of Ord by flying around the center of Nebraska barnstorming. She met new people and talked about the ever-growing city of Ord. During some trips, Evelyn landed inside the small towns or in nearby fields and valleys. Because people heard the airplane's drone overhead or read in the newspaper that she would appear, they rushed from their cars, homes, businesses, or farms. They crowded around the Ord and Evelyn while they talked to her, asked for autographs, or studied the plane.

Evelyn posed for photos and then offered sky rides for free. Her popularity especially grew when she took her dog, Scottie, along. He stole the show and encouraged others to take a ride. But since she was not yet a licensed professional pilot, so she could not accept money from passengers. That was a major problem since she needed to earn money to make payments on the plane. At least she recorded increased flight hours which were needed to earn a professional pilot's license.

Another stumbling block changed Evelyn's plans. Jack Jefford decided to move to Alaska in 1937. "Evelyn, I know you won't have anyone to study with, but I simply want a different adventure. My dream has been to be a bush pilot, and I will work for an air taxi firm in Nome."

The young woman understood dreams and thanked Jefford for all his knowledge. "You became a trusted friend; I will always remember you." But without Jefford, Evelyn leaned on her limited experiences to study weight scales, engine workings, plane construction, weather, and navigation. Finally, she and her father drove to the airport in Lincoln, Nebraska to take the pilots' exam. After completion, she learned that she did not pass strategic parts of the test. Evelyn stood frozen. "I didn't pass. I'm not going to get a license." Her brain seemed fuzzy, and she thought she would faint. *No! Get a hold of your wits. Use your brain like when going to a spin in the airplane.*

Evelyn pushed her trembling hands into her pockets. She grimaced and hoped the officials believed it was a smile. Evelyn thanked them, turned around, and forced her legs to walk out to her father's waiting car. John Sharp scrutinized the downcast eyes and Evelyn's stiff walk. When she climbed into the automobile, John reached out his hand. "You are used to always coming out on top the first time you try. But there are occasions when you can't. This is one example." Evelyn's shoulders shuddered, and she covered her face. "But daughter, you possess one important factor. You are not a quitter. You have perseverance and determination. Just like after a losing basketball game, you must review what went wrong and then fix it."

Evelyn nodded and wiped the tears off her face. "You're right. I'll try again, don't worry." But when reached her home, she rushed up the stairs to her bedroom. She lay on her bed and sobbed. Devasted, Evelyn didn't know how to face her friends. When Evelyn rejoined her parents in the kitchen, she had a plan. "I'll retake the test, but I'm going to need an instructor which needs money. But since I still don't have a professional pilot's license, I can't charge for rides." Her parents didn't offer any advice. Their daughter needed to make her own decisions this time. Tears welled in Evelyn's eyes, and she laid her head on the table. "I'm afraid I can't make the payments for my plane."

"Daughter, sometimes this happens in a new endeavor."

"But I let the citizens of Ord down. They made such a gift of the downpayment. I am so embarrassed. I can't face anyone."

Mary Sharp placed her warm hand on Evelyn's arm. "Did you fail on purpose?"

Evelyn's head snapped up and her eyes squinted. "What? Why are you accusing me?"

"I'm not." Mary kept her voice soft and low. "So, if you didn't try to flunk, how could it be your fault?" Mary smiled at her daughter's frown. "No one could fail if they had tried their best. You didn't pass because you didn't have all the information."

Evelyn jumped up from her chair and enveloped her mother in a hug. "Thanks, Mama. You're right. I didn't win the game, but I gave it a good go."

A knock came at the kitchen door and before anyone answered, Irene rushed in. "Did ya get it? Are you licensed?" Then she noticed her best friend's face. "Oh, Evelyn, it's okay."

"I feel so silly. Everyone will laugh now."

"Come on, Evelyn, when did you become a whiner?" Irene put her face near Evelyn's and glared into her friend's eyes. "No body in this whole town or county could have passed one or two parts of that test. Did you really think you were that much better than us?"

Evelyn's eyes were wide, and her mouth gapped open. "No. But, I don't know."

Irene wrapped her arms around her friend and howled with laughter. "Oh, Evelyn. We all love you. But we all knew you were human too." The two girls stepped back and continued giggling.

"Irene, you're a pain in the neck." Mary and John shook their heads and chuckled.

Two days later, Evelyn asked her father to join the meeting with Dr. Auble. Evelyn told herself that she wouldn't cry. She needed to act like a calm, responsible person. After Evelyn gave Dr. Auble the information about the test, he reached out his hand and shook hers.

"No, this was a business transaction. We perceived the risks." Dr. Auble soothed Evelyn's feelings of guilt. "I saw you work hard and conduct all those barnstorming trips. Evelyn, you're still young. You will figure it out. I have trust."

On the saddest day of her life was in January 1938. A devasted Evelyn Sharp sold The Ord. Her hand trembled as she signed the ownership papers. *I know people say, I tried, But I failed. I should have found a way. I must attend flight school. But how can I afford it? I need business advice.*

After a discussion with Dr. Auble and other business minds, Evelyn asked for a town meeting. The notice went out, and the auditorium was filled with friends of ages. Evelyn Sharp, home-town girl, stepped up to the microphone and gathered her courage. She gazed out into the crowd of the small-town residents. She recognized those who bought ice cream from her when she was ten years old. There were the faces of local farm families who had met her during her barn-storming events. School friends and teachers – aware of Evelyn's determination and competitiveness – waited to hear her remarks. "You know me, I don't like to be a grandstander." She paused and waited for the reaction. Her school pals whistled and hooted in fun.

"You love being the star!"

"You do your best work in a battle," her best friend, Irene, shouted and waved.

"Evelyn Sharp, a shrinking violet, no way!" The principal of the high school and a group of teachers all joked.

Evelyn chuckled with the crowd. But then her face lost its smile. "The city of Ord allowed me to grow up as normal girl - oh maybe a little cockeyed at times." Snickers continued from the audience. She grinned down at the hall filled with her supporters. "I was able to enjoy many things in life. This town has blessed me with sports, music, and swimming in the river." More hoots rang out. "And of course, I appreciated my friends who put up with my running out to the airport in between music contests and sporting games." Evelyn paused and surveyed the different faces while the audience remained silent and waited for her next words. She took a deep breath. With a passionate and determined voice, she called out. "But I just love to fly!" Every applauded and cheered.

When the audience calmed, she continued. "The last time I took the aviation test, I passed some parts. But I didn't have the right knowledge for the rest of the exam. I need help understanding weight scales, engine workings, plane construction, weather, and navigation." People nodded and murmured to each other. "I'm not trying to pass the buck, but I need a professional instructor to fully learn this information." She paused and allowed her audience time for consideration. "I am determined to obtain a professional pilot's license." Evelyn's voice echoed. "I am willing to study and learn. But to do so, I need attend a flight school."

The air in the auditorium became heavy with indecision. A confused murmur rippled through the crowd. Her voice called out again. "One-hundred dollars isn't peanuts, but I cannot continue to learn new facts whenever an instructor happens to be around." Evelyn Sharp stepped away from the microphone and approached the front of the stage, "I need your help!" Again, the applause roared with encouragement. The town of Ord loved their home-town female aviator.

Dr. Auble, who had been standing at the back of the stage, now stepped forward. "Citizens of Ord, Evelyn is not asking you to dig into your pockets. But she needs ideas on how to raise some funds. I know you are resilient. Let's break into groups and discuss different fund-raising ideas so that Evelyn Sharp can attend flight school." The atmosphere was filled with conversation and inspiration.

Thirty minutes later, one group marched to the auditorium stage and faced the citizens. The spokesperson began. "Our group considered holding a benefit dance." Murmurs of approval and nods followed. He continued, "Citizens from all around could come to the auditorium and have a fun time. Something we all need these days." The many faces nodded their agreement. "Donated food and drinks would be for sale. Ladies, how about holding an old-fashioned bake sale during the dance? I'm sure others have clever ideas too."

During the 1930s and 1940s, Americans had little money. Lessons learned from the Depression taught friends and neighbors that one person couldn't achieve much without the help of others.

Communities supported events which offered the common folk fun and camaraderie. The applause implied the audience's agreement and approval of the suggestions. Dr. Auble immediately created committees.

Three weeks later – from two counties around Ord and beyond – town people, farmers, couples, singles, older people, and young kids arrived for the dance. The Ord city auditorium buzzed with music by a local band and from a record player. The sizable crowd danced the two-step, jitterbug, polkas, and waltzes. By the end of evening, Dr. Auble used the band's microphone. "Ladies and gentlemen, with the generous help of so many Ord citizens, this benefit has raised close to one hundred dollars." Friends, family, and guests all applauded and cheered.

"Hot diggity Dog!" Evelyn cheered with tears in her eyes. "Irene, it's enough money for flight lessons!"

Irene hugged her old friend. "See how much Ord loves you."

Evelyn rushed to the stage and thanked everyone in attendance. John Sharp tried to shake every man's hand. Mary Sharp wiped her tears with a flower-patterned handkerchief.

Within a week, Evelyn registered for classes at the Lincoln Airplane and Flying School in Lincoln, Nebraska. She was the one female among seventy-five males. The landing strip laid north to south on what would later become 19th Street in Lincoln between the streets of Van Dorn and Calvert. Her parents found a family in Lincoln with whom Evelyn could rent a room. Evelyn Sharp was ready to move on toward her dreams.

"Hey, what's buzzin' cousin?" At lunch, a male student strolled passed Evelyn who usually ate alone. "Don't you know that other girls have tried this school." The other male students listened, elbowed each other, and slapped their knees. The cocky student continued. "But they always failed and quit." Evelyn Sharp raised her face, grinned, but remained silent. As she continued her lunch, other males hooted and jeered. Then a young man sat down across the table, leaned on his elbows, and grinned. "What makes you so special? Why will you succeed?"

Evelyn smirked, "You don't know how stubborn I am." Again, the boys hooted and chortled. Evelyn rose from the seat and picked up her tray. "I am going to be here long enough to earn a license. So, get used to it." She lifted her chin and challenged her male co-students with a smile. "I'll be cooking with gas and flying circles around you guys in no time at all!"

The classmates elbowed each other. The student chuckled, "You've got moxie, little girl." Evelyn proved her knowledge of aviation day after day. In time, she was part of the gang. They all enjoyed flying through the clouds and into the wind. Eventually her male co-students drove to her boarding house each morning, honked their horn, and gave Evelyn a ride to flight classes. Evelyn thrived with her new knowledge about weights, measuring, and how to read maps. As in high school, Evelyn was a quick-study and exhibited her competitive attitude.

In a surprise letter in April 1938, Evelyn received an invitation to be a special guest for the Capitol Theater in Grand Island, Nebraska.

"They want me to attend the grand opening of the movie, *Test Pilot*." Evelyn lowered the letter and stared at her new friends. "Why?"

"Whoa, why didn't we get invites?" One of her male friends hooted at lunch time.

"I guess it's because I was Nebraska's youngest pilot. Sorry." She wrinkled her nose and snickered. The new film starred Clark Gable, Myrna Loy, and Spencer Tracy - famous movie stars in the 1930's and 1940's. Evelyn and three girlfriends, along with her boarding family as chaperones, drove to Grand Island. When Evelyn arrived, she was given a telegram. "Holy mackerel!" Evelyn's fingers trembled as she tore open the telegram. She turned to her friends and beamed, "The actors all signed the telegram. I'm never going to lose this piece of paper!" The movie went on to be a national success.

In May 1938, after weeks of intense learning and studying, Evelyn passed the transport pilot's test and earned her Commercial license No. 34711. Evelyn could now charge for plane rides and earn money. Because of this new success, a banquet was held in her honor. Charles Doyle, Secretary of Nebraska's Aeronautics Commission, presented the transport license. "Evelyn Sharp," Doyle announced, "has become the youngest female licensed commercial pilot in Nebraska as well as in the nation! Congratulations, Miss Sharp. You have made history." While everyone – including her parents – applauded, Evelyn remembered the little girl who listened to the radio and declared that she would be a pilot someday.

The next step in Evelyn's plans was to accept a position to carry the U.S. mail. She flew from town to town in Nebraska the next summer and carried mail bags to each location. On May 19, 1938, Evelyn Sharp – nineteen- years-old – marched out to her plane dressed in black boots, breeches, and a special jacket worn by air mail pilots. Evelyn chuckled when she glimpsed at her mother. The color faded from Mary's face when she noticed that Evelyn wore a pistol strapped on her right hip. "Don't worry, Mama, this gun will protect the U.S. mail. Remember, I learned to shoot a long time ago."

Evelyn flew the first leg of an air mail flight from Grand Island to North Loup. After pictures and speeches, Evelyn flew a second mail bag to Ord. By delivering over 2,500 letters from Grand Island and the North Loup Valley communities that summer, Evelyn Sharp became the first and only woman mail pilot in America.

Since Evelyn earned money from delivering the mail and on other days taking paid passengers up in her plane, she saved enough money to purchase a Curtis Robin OX-5. This airplane had been originally owned by the infamous "Wrong Way" Corrigan. Douglas Corrigan was an aviator who in 1938 flew from Long Beach, California to New York City. There was no problem with that flight. But then he flew from Brooklyn to Ireland which was not in his flight plan which is illegal. Corrigan claimed the cloud cover confused him, but most believed he flew to Ireland on purpose. After that, he was referred to as Wrong Way.

"Just don't do any flights that aren't approved." John Sharp laughed at Evelyn's purchase. She smiled. *Life is good. My dream has come true.*

CHAPTER 8

A Career in the Clouds

On February 4, 1939, Evelyn celebrated the fourth anniversary of her first flight lesson. During that time, Evelyn had broken records and made history. Reporters rushed to the Ord airport and surrounded the aviator. "Evelyn how was the last two years of barnstorming?"

"Yeah," another called out, "do you still like flying?"

Evelyn leaned against the wing of her plane and thought about her answer. "I've landed in so many small Nebraska towns I don't need a map anymore."

The reporters laughed. "Any regrets?"

"The barnstorming at county fairs and rodeos was fun. I met so many people. I've given over five thousand rides to passengers while charging one dollar a ride or seventy-five cents for high school girls." Then she shook her head. "It's crazy, but some days I piloted over ninety passengers." But then her face turned serious as she confessed. "But lately, I've been concerned about the risks of barnstorming. In some locations, I fly between newly added power lines and past taller town buildings." The crowd murmured and nodded. "But I don't regret the opportunity to earn flying hours and meeting so many Nebraskans." Privately, Eveyln didn't want to take those risks anymore. *I need a real job in aviation.*

On March 1, 1939, Evelyn and Mary Sharp drove to Fort Worth, Texas for a national aviation meeting of the Ninety-Nines. Thirty-four women attended along with Evelyn who was still the youngest pilot. During one of the meeting breaks, Jacqueline Cochran – an ace test pilot who had set air speed records – took Evelyn to the side. "Listen, Evelyn, even though you have accomplished so much, you still need to acquire more experience and flying hours." Evelyn nodded and leaned closer to hear her advice. "You need to build a portfolio of your experiences in aviation. Create a scrapbook of dates of accomplishments. Record dates of certificates and licenses. Lastly, you need references from other professional pilots and airport managers."

"Yes, you're right. But how do I get references from other than Nebraska people? Some may think their references might be biased."

"One tactic is contacting aviation schools and seeking out a position as an instructor. Those experiences and flight records would be good references. You'd also gain lots of hours in the air."

Later as Evelyn talked with other working pilots, she realized she lacked experience in map reading. "The knowledge and experience you gain might save your life one day." Amelia Earhart stared into the young woman's eyes. "Experience in map reading is key especially when flying over water."

In a few weeks, Evelyn contacted the Lincoln aviation school and asked if the school needed an instructor. The owner had just returned from Washington, D.C. where he collaborated with aeronautical officials. "I realized that interest in aviation is growing." His voice boomed over the telephone. "I recently started the Civilian Pilot Training Program (CPTP). But you know, there were not enough instructors." Evelyn listened and hoped for good news. "Of course, Evelyn, I need instructors. There are opportunities all over the nation for pilots like you. I can get you names and phone numbers."

In no time, Evelyn accepted a position as a temporary trainer CPTP program in Mitchell, South Dakota. During 1940, Evelyn worked as an instructor with the Government's pre-W.W. II Civilian Pilot Training Program. So off she moved with her parents to Spearfish, South Dakota – close to Mt. Rushmore and Devil's Tower. After a year, Evelyn had news. "Papa, can you believe it? I have trained over 350 male students and most of them will enter the military. But guess what, I have accepted a new position."

"What?" Her mother's head jerked up from the newspaper. "But I thought you loved teaching aviation techniques." Confused, Mary Sharp gawked at her daughter.

"I do. But I'm ready to learn more. Are you two ready to move to California?"

Mary put her hands to her face and grinned, "California, here I come!"

At Bakersfield, California, Evelyn – the youngest of ten licensed female flying instructors – taught flying courses. But she thought teaching wasn't enough. *I'm right here where there are great instructors. I can learn more.* "I can't believe you are taking classes in aerobatic flying." One of her co-workers teased her. "Do you have time to sleep? You can't possibly fit dating into your schedule."

Evelyn snickered, "I love to fly. I want to learn more and challenge myself more." But secretly, her plan involved two steps. First,
she attended classes in advanced aviation classes and gained as
much knowledge about piloting planes as she could. The second
part was to earn as many flight hours as possible. She wanted to be
ready if any new opportunities opened.

A reporter approached Sharp on the Bakersfield tarmac. "Hey,
Evelyn, if America becomes involved in the war, do you think
women pilots could really be an asset?"

Evelyn glared and counted to ten. "Of course. Women pilots
could serve in several areas of military programs. I will do whatever
is asked of me; and I know my fellow aviators will too."

On December 7, 1941, Evelyn, along with her female aviation
friends, listened to the radio in the hangar. They, like the rest of
America, were stunned as they listened about the Japanese assault.
"I wonder if any of our past student pilots were there at the Navy
base in Pearl Harbor, Hawaii?"

One female instructor glanced at her comrades. "This will not
end well. Ladies, we may be thrust into a war situation." A shiver
rushed up Evelyn's spine, and her heart realized that her friend's
prediction would change America. The female aviators quietly
readied themselves for whatever duty would be needed. Days later,
America entered World War II. The American government and
Military experts began making critical decisions and the security
of American.

The military officials first appointed Bakersfield, California as
the center base for military aircraft and issued rules for civilian pilots. Non-military Americans needed to relocate their airplanes at
least 150 miles inland from the Pacific Ocean so that their take-offs

and flying patterns would not interfere with military activity. But not all civilian owners were able to reach their planes. Evelyn and her fellow instructors were asked to fly the private planes to Long Pine, California. This new need for flying skills changed the direction of Evelyn's aviation career.

Citizens of America, young and old, adjusted to the demands of World War II. America's military supplies were woefully inadequate. Caught unprepared, the Air Force had kept just 1,100 planes fit for combat. In addition, flying instructors or training facilities were limited. Factories and shipyards went into action and operated twenty-four hours a day, seven days a week. To save resources for the war needs, civilians were issued restrictions - called rations - on items like gasoline, shoes, rubber tires. Tin can and rubber tire drives were organized. Citizens brought their used tires and tin cans to specific locations, then the gathered materials were sent to factories and used in building planes.

Most men under thirty years were now drafted for the war. There was a shortage of laborers for factories and weapon munition sites. American women stepped up and filled needed jobs breaking society's opinion that married women were not supposed to work outside the home. "I am proud of American women." Evelyn told a reporter. "Everyone is needed, and women can do it."

All during World War II, women worked in shipyards and airplane factories. The image of Rosie the Riveter became symbolic of American women who stepped up to the plate, learned new skills, and dirtied their hands. Evelyn and her women aviation colleagues would also do their part.

CHAPTER 9

The Ninety-Nines to the Rescue

E velyn's female, aviation comrades jumped at the opportunity to aid America. Jacqueline Cochran created an aviation plan which used female aviators. She met with President Franklin Roosevelt, Eleanor Roosevelt, and General Henry Arnold. There she proposed that the members of the Ninety-Nines would help the United States military by flying newly manufactured war planes across the country to military bases. Because of military red tape and lack of male cooperation, Cochran's suggestion became stagnant.

However, Canada and Great Britian used Cochran's plan to create their own Air Transport Auxiliary. While moving planes in Europe, the female aviators dealt with German attacks and harsh weather. Navigating without radio contact, the pilots used maps and memorized landmarks thus proving their valuable skills. Adding to these difficulties, the Royal Air Force used 120 diverse types of aircraft. "These women are not regular pilots." Cochran told the news reporters. "These women are the best of the best!"

The husband of pilot Nancy Harkness Love worked at the Pentagon with Colonel William H. Tunner who oversaw the acquirement of experienced pilots for the war effort. Because he had trouble finding qualified male pilots, Tunner joked one day. "Lowe, doesn't you wife fly? She can fly for us too." Lowe chuckled. Fully aware that his wife was an accomplished pilot, he also remembered that she had worked as a test pilot with the well-known air racer Frank Hawks.

"Sir, my wife served as the test pilot for the now standard tricycle landing gear." When Tunner's eyebrows raised with interest, Lowe continued. Nancy also orchestrated the effort to paint the names of towns on their water towers as a navigational aid for pilots."

Tunner's mouth dropped open. "Really, she was the one who did that?"

Lowe nodded. "My wife's aviation skills are more than adequate."

Colonel Tunner slapped his desk. "Ask your wife if she knows of any female pilots who want to fly for us."

Nancy Love flew into action. She collaborated with female pilots and military officials to create a squadron of women pilots. But she still faced resistance. "Mrs. Love, you know the problems women face when they fly." One military official argued. "Women don't have the physical stamina. Plus," he winked at Love, "they couldn't use the cockpit relief tubes."

"Sir," Love clenched her jaw and hid her frustration, "those are old myths." She raised her chin and stared at the officer. "Women have flown for years without those old ideas causing any problems."

The officer's face reddened. "Well, okay. But when away from their home bases, the women can't sleep in the men's bunkhouses."

"Sir, I think we can also manage that minor problem."

However, resistance from male military officials continued. As a result, the creation of a women's squadron made no progress. The paperwork sat on some official's desk. That is until the President's wife, Eleanor Roosevelt, supported the idea of women aviators. Using her daily newspaper column on September 1, 1942, Eleanor authored the article, *My Day,* which advocated for the female pilots and their cause.

She argued that the frivolous worries about their abilities were not as important as the need for experienced pilots. Because of Eleanor Roosevelt's popularity with the American people and her political power, government officials agreed.

On September 5, 1942, telegrams were sent to the eighty-three women pilots who had earned over five hundred flying hours. The telegram asked that the pilots, including Evelyn Sharp, apply to be part of the Army-related group called the Women's Auxiliary Ferrying Squadron. The female pilots would airplanes from the factory assembly lines to United States and Canadian military bases. Now twenty-three-years old, Evelyn answered a reporter. "I am honored to be part of this squadron." The local newspaper also printed Evelyn's second passionate response. "The squadron is a serious opportunity to serve my country in time of war."

The requirements of the Women's Auxiliary Ferrying Squadron were rigorous. Female pilots were required to be American citizens between the ages of 21 and 35 years old and had passed a required medical exam. The pilots provided documentation of flying over five hundred hours and had piloted high-powered engines. Meeting the criteria, Evelyn Sharp joined the program on October 20, 1942, as the seventeenth woman pilot accepted into the WAFS. The twenty-five members became known as *The Originals*. Evelyn Sharp had 2,968 hours of flying time, more than the other pilots. "This is such an honor." Evelyn hugged her teammates.

The ground-breaking squadron was first sent to Newcastle Army Air Base in Wilmington, Delaware. The pilots were told they needed to learn the *Army Way*. These young women pilots were some of the most experienced pilots in America – male or female – and each had recorded over 1200 average hours in the air. Sadly, they were not considered members of the military. "I am furious!" Esther Manning exploded to her colleagues. "We're expected to follow military rules and procedures, but we're not good enough to be called Army pilots."

"Did you read this?" Dorothy Scott pointed to the printed rules. "If a female pilot disobeys any of the rules, she will be kicked out of the program."

Evelyn had also read through the materials. "The same, old stereotypes we've heard before. The answer is to simply fly better than all the rest."

The trainees received khaki flight overalls, a parachute, goggles, and a white silk AAF flying scarf. "Get a load of these overalls!" Mary Helen Clark raised her hand and displayed her khaki suit. "We'll look like those men in Harlem wearing zoot suits!"

"Hey, yeah, they do." Cackled Evelyn. "It's a great name."

From then on, the female pilots nicknamed their flying overalls "the zoot suits." For four weeks, the female pilots were trained in the military rules. They were taught how to stand guard, and the proper way to march. "Hours spent on marching instead of flying, I don't get it." Cornelia Fort grumbled one night. Cornelia had worked in a civilian training position at Pearl Harbor on December 7, 1941. That morning, the twenty-two-year-old pilot was in the air flying with a student. "I noticed an airplane headed fast and straight into our direction. I jammed the throttle open, forced the plan upward, and escaped the collision."

A silence fell over her comrades as Cornelia shared her experience. "When the plane flew past, I recognized the Japanese flag on the wings." She shook her head and lowered her eyes. "Then I noticed dozens of fighter planes moving in formation toward the harbor."

The room was silent as her teammates listened, and she paused to gather her emotions. "I will always remember watching as a silver device detached from one airplane. At first, I didn't realize what it was." her lips trembled. "Then the bomb exploded in the middle of the harbor." Her eyes welled with tears. "We women can do so much more to help this war than marching."

Daily, the pilots attended classes in navigation. Pilot Betty Huyler Gillies's records indicated all her fourteen years of flying experience and the total sum of 1400 flying hours. She shook her head. "You know, I can understand that we need to learn these lessons. They are important. But the superiors forget that we have been flying for years. I have earned several aeronautical ratings; but here, I am not recognized as a qualified pilot."

In addition, the female pilots learned transfer routes, the recording of data, and military jargon. Since the early military planes did not have radios or instruments, the female aviators learned map-reading, landmark recognition, and the use of a parachute. Although most of the women had already flown several diverse types of aircrafts, they needed to demonstrate their abilities in flying airplanes like the PT-19 Fairchild as well as larger planes such as the P-38 and P-51 which were Mustang, single-engine fighter aircraft.

Nancy Love became the first woman to prove her proficiency in all the Army Air Forces' complex, high performance aircraft. She mastered the P-521 Mustang and the P-38 Lightning fighters. Other members followed her example and learned the operation of the four- engine B-17 Flying Fortress. "Finally," Nancy Batson sighed. "They provided some decent clothes for open cockpits." She held up two new uniforms which consisted of a one-piece military jump suit for use in the summer months and long-zippered, leather pants and jacket for the winter.

Evelyn cheered, "Thank goodness for the lined gloves." Added to the uniform were goggles, leather helmets, facemasks, and heavy wool-lined boots. The squadron was also required to use firearms. "I hunted while a kid in Nebraska." Evelyn shared. "But these pistols are quite the weapon."

After passing all the tests and procedures, the female trainees were called *WAFS,* short for *Women's Auxiliary Ferrying Squadron.* Now they wore a gray-green uniform including a jacket, shirt, skirt or pants, cap, military patches, and silver-wing pins. The women grinned at each other. "Well, ladies, we look professional and feel proud." Evelyn grinned at her team. "I know we deserve it." The teammates applauded.

The WAFs lived in barracks filled with rows of beds and little privacy. A group shower and bathroom completed the living arrangement. Evelyn and other women pilots received a mere $250 a month. "I'm sorry, ladies," Nancy Love shook her head. "We earn $600 less than civilian men earn doing the same job."

The WAFS first duties included delivering airplanes across America and Canada. On September 14, 1942, General Henry Arnold of the Army Air Force agreed to use Jackie Cochran's original plan. He installed her as the director of the women's flying training located at Avenger Field in Sweetwater, Texas. This group, like the WAFS, ferried military planes. There, Delphine Bohn commanded the 601st Squadron of the Women Airforce Service Pilots. The duties assigned to women pilots had hidden dangers. Each day, the pilots towed targets and banners across the sky for machine gun practice. Since machine guns used live ammunition, the pilots often reported that stray bullets hit their planes. The risks of flying for the military were clear and present.

In March 1943, a ferrying mission used a combination of male and female pilots. A young male pilot flew his plane too close to Cornelia Fort's plane. In error, his plane clipped off her wing. The male pilot's slightly damaged plane was able to fly and landed successfully. Since Fort's plane missed a complete wing, it banked into a spin and crashed. Fort became the first WAF pilot killed in a plane crash during the war. Although the accident was ruled as not Fort's fault, another pilot's mistake cost her life.

The most dangerous jobs involved serving as test pilots for newly manufactured planes. When an airplane came out of the factory, a pilot would fly them to a designed air base.

Shared aviation knowledge embraced the theory that if a plane was apt to have a problem, the incident would occur in the first routine flights especially during takeoffs and landings. The risks were high. Evelyn and the others understood the dangers; they simply loved flying.

CHAPTER 10

Dreams and Dangers

During 1943, Evelyn Sharp thrived in the aviation environment. *This is where I belong. My dream has come true. I am the luckiest girl from Nebraska.* Pushing herself as usual, she set a goal to fly every type of airplane in the military. Qualified to fly heavy cargo in transport plans, Evelyn advanced to flying bombers and attack planes. Evelyn and three other female pilots were qualified to fly the A-20 plane nicknamed 'the mankiller.' She became the first woman to transport the plane from coast to coast.

The Army decided to join the two groups of female aviators and form the *WASP - Women Airforce Service Pilots*. But women pilots were still not acknowledged as miliary pilots. "We still aren't members of the military." Evelyn complained to her comrades. "We do the same work as the men. We also have more flying hours and additional ratings than some of the male pilots." The women were frustrated and could not understand the reasoning. In addition to less pay and no military recognition, the women pilots had no military insurance or military benefits.

"What happens if we get hurt?" One female pilot questioned. "Who pays for our health care?" No one knew the answer.

In June 1943, Evelyn had qualified to pilot a P-51 Mustang. Built with two tails or split tails, the plane used three landing gears like a tricycle. Next Evelyn earned her qualifications to fly the fast P-38 Lightening which most pilots considered difficult. The plane had two engines for speed, but sometimes the engines quit working in mid-air. If the plane wasn't at a high enough altitude, it would bank into a spin and crash. Engine changes were completed. But during take-off, the aircraft was still considered a dangerous plane. Because of their large fuel tanks, both the P-38 and the Mustang could escort other planes over longer distances. In no time, Evelyn had recorded over 3,500 flying hours and now could be assigned to pilot the B-17, the Flying Fortress.

Because each plane weighed between 32,000 and 55,000 pounds, military officials believed that women not physically strong enough to manage the planes. Of course, this belief irritated Evelyn. After hours of difficult practice, she earned her Fifth Rating – the highest level for ferrying pilots.

When the airplane factories reported that several airplanes were waiting for transport, two hundred pilots were qualified including Barbara Erickson and Evelyn Sharp. In late March 1944, Evelyn was assigned to ferry the P-39 from California to Newark, New Jersey. Evelyn Sharp never turned down an assignment, no matter how dangerous. With her hours of flying experience – the equivalent of flying a plane one-hundred-twenty times back and forth across America – she was ready for any new mission. "I'm supposed to fly the P-39 Lightning twin-engine fighter on a five-day flight schedule," she told her roommates. "My flying hours will add up fast."

"Oh, that's a long trip especially in the plane! Be careful."

"Of course, you know how particular I am about checking out the planes before and after each flight."

During the last week of March 1944, Evelyn Sharp lifted off in the P-39 Lightning ready to complete her mission. At each stop, Evelyn refueled, checked the engines, and the oil pressure. She inspected the wing flaps and other pertinent checks. When she felt the plane was set for the next day, she stayed overnight in a hotel or at one of the air bases. Like years before, Evelyn's routine involved recording all the details in her logbook. During the fourth day while headed to Harris, Pennsylvania, Sharp encountered a snowstorm combined with rain and sleet. Although Evelyn had earned an instrumental rating, military rules stipulated that women transport pilots were not allowed to fly solo in severe weather. Following orders, she located the New Cumberland airfield near Beacon Hill, landed, and stayed the rest of the day. While waiting for the weather to clear, Evelyn Sharp wrote several letters to friends and family. The next morning, she mailed them off.

During the next morning's breakfast, Evelyn sat with a male pilot. "Hey, over the past few days one of my engines acted up." She stirred her eggs. "What do you think?" She waited to hear his advice.

"Well, you know the plane's reputation." He glanced up from his coffee and scrunched his forehead. "Check it over carefully. I've never seen such a fickle plane."

"I always do, but I'll give this a thorough second inspection."

On March 30, 1944, Evelyn Sharp marched into the airplane hangar and completed her flight ritual. But that morning, she checked and rechecked the plane. Others testified that Evelyn focused on the twin engines and tires. "Well," she called out to the other pilots in the hanger, "guess everything's tip top. I've checked everything I can." Once in the cockpit, she went through her precheck one more time. *Everything checks out. Guess I'll finish the flight.* As she taxied to the airstrip, Evelyn radioed the control tower. "Final check shows no problems with the engines."

Airplanes usually take off against the wind so that the air will move faster under the wings and give the plane more lift into the air. But that day, the wind blew from the wrong direction. The control tower instructed Evelyn to take-off *uphill* meaning with the wind. When taking off with a headwind, the air current slows down the plane during its acceleration. But headwind also increases the flow of air over the wings, allowing the plane take off in a shorter distance and climb in a sharper angle in order to clear any obstacle. However, the impact of headwind and tailwind on an airplane can be significant. The air current affects the takeoff and landing performance because the wind shear – which is the sudden change in wind direction or speed – can cause turbulence and make flying conditions challenging and dangerous. The lucky pilot from Nebraska wasn't fazed, she had taken off in all types of weather.

Evelyn pushed back the plane's throttle, rumbled down the runway, and lifted off at 10:29 a.m. One minute after take-off, 10:30 a.m., the aircraft flew at under seven hundred feet. While flying into the more difficult uphill maneuver, one of the P-39 Lightning's 1,325 horsepower twin-engines stopped working. Evelyn Sharp's vast experience told her that a plane missing an engine would flip over, fly into a tailspin, and plummet toward the ground. The skilled pilot also knew that her plane flew too close to the ground. There wasn't time to use her parachute and escape the cockpit. Evelyn Sharp's brain searched all her past flying experiences. Her mind raced through all the knowledge she gained in flight school. She needed an extraordinary plan.

Evelyn jammed the rudder pedal and fought against the spin. But after the plane leveled out, the aircraft still did not have enough altitude. Sadly, if her plane had flown five additional feet of altitude before the engine lost its power, Evelyn could have managed the tailspin and landed without a problem. But now, Sharp realized her situation was grave. Evelyn's eyes frantically searched for a landing spot. Houses lined the ground on one side of the plane. Radio towers and trees were on the other. Banking the plane 180 degrees back toward the airport, Evelyn flew the plane at a dangerously low altitude. "Mayday, mayday! I'm coming in too low!"

Her experienced hands gripped the steering wheel when one of her wings snagged a tree branch. Again, her brain searched through all her experiences and knowledge. Evelyn Sharp decided her one possibility was to land the plane in a wheels-up position called "a pancake." This landing position meant that she would drop the airplane down on its belly and slide to a stop.

However, the crippled plane descended too fast. When the aircraft crashed onto its belly, the plane skidded along the ground for ten feet and then stopped near Middleton, Pennsylvania. Within seconds, rescue personnel and a local farmer rushed to rescue Evelyn. Smoke poured out of the failed left engine. Miraculously, the plane itself had slight damage. The pilot's aeronautical skills saved the plane.

Rescue personnel rushing to the plane watched as the local farmer carried Evelyn Sharp's body from the plane. The talented pilot was dead. The nose of the P-38 had hit the ground ahead of the two engine nacelles or frames. The plane's steering column was rammed up through the cockpit. The violent thrust broke the pilot's seat and threw Evelyn through the canopy. Her neck was broken, and Evelyn Sharp died instantly.

At age twenty-four years and a mere seven years after her first flight, Evelyn Sharp died in a flash of time. The girl from the Sandhills of Nebraska was only three flights from receiving her fifth rating - the highest certificate then available to women. Evelyn Sharp had defied the odds of a limited future.

Against stereotypes and cultural barriers, Evelyn dared to dreamed big. With determination and enthusiasm, the small-town girl celebrated life and thrived through her passion of aviation. Despite her early death, Evelyn Sharp had made history – not just records and numbers. Evelyn became a role-model for young women, then and today.

CHAPTER II

A Hero's Welcome

E velyn, like the other women pilots, was not eligible for Army death benefits. A bill had been introduced in Congress during 1944 to militarize the WASPs, but a few key individuals and a famed columnist, Drew Pearson, opposed the bill. As a result, the bill became blocked. The women pilots were simply employees. Now Evelyn's grieving WASP comrades needed money to send Evelyn's body back to Ord, Nebraska. At the nearby ferrying base of New Castle, Delaware, the women pilots took up a collection and raised $200. This small amount would cover the train fare to send Evelyn's body home and help with the funeral costs.

"I don't care if we women don't get military burial honors," Squadron Commander Betty Gillies insisted, "we are going to send a uniformed representative to stand at her funeral. Evelyn deserves it!" Commander Gillies arranged for a train ticket, and asked Nancy Batson to travel 1,367 miles over two, long days to Ord, Nebraska with Evelyn's body. Nancy Batson had openly acknowledged that Evelyn was one of the best pilots she had ever known. But she wasn't prepared to witness the influence her young friend had in her hometown.

After the train rambled across the rolling Nebraska plains, it slowed as it approached Ord, Nebraska. Curiously, Nancy Batson looked out the window for her first glimpse of Evelyn's hometown. She could not believe her eyes. The train station's platform bowed from the weight of the crowd awaiting the train. Hundreds of additional grieving Nebraskans surrounded the platform and lined along the tracks waiting to receive Evelyn's body. The tear-stained faces of young and old mourned their hometown girl.

While at the funeral home, Nancy gazed around the room with wide eyes and shook her head in amazement. Person after person approached the uniformed, young pilot with stories and remembrances of Evelyn. "I couldn't believe all the stories." Batson later told her squad's members. "Evelyn was a remarkable woman and my dear friend, but I never grasped how she affected the lives of so many people."

As the WAF's representative, Nancy remained at the funeral home for Evelyn's parents' support. A young man, who identified himself as Evelyn's former classmate raised his chin high. "Well, it's the way we do things in small towns."

An older woman approached Nancy. "Evelyn took part in so much of the town's history. Everyone considered her family."

A quiet older man approached Nancy Batson. He had held his hat in his hands and waited for a break in her conversation. "Miss," he reached out his wrinkled hand, "I would like to ask you if I can drape an American flag on Evelyn's casket?" Stunned, Nancy was lost for words. Her mind whirled. This wasn't an official military funeral. Evelyn wasn't allowed government insurance. The dedicated pilot wasn't given any death benefits or officially entitled to military death honors. There would be no honor guard, no gun salute, or flag folding. Her neck and face flushed. She was angry with the injustice of the system.

Batson eyes studied the quiet-spoken man. The sincerity of the man's gesture and his request had nothing to do with the military. It had everything to do with the respect of one American for another American. "Sir, I see no reason why you can't." Nancy Bates was touched by his personal act of respect for Evelyn's service. She shook his hand and thanked him on behalf of Evelyn and her other women comrades. Evelyn's funeral lasted two and a half hours. High school friends, sport teammates, school officials, and town folk offered eulogies which included stories of fun times. People shared stories about her competitive nature during sports and chuckled during remembrances of a young Evelyn Sharp selling ice cream cones. Evelyn's spirit and passion for life touched many lives. Before the funeral ended, the mayor of Ord stepped up to the lectern. "I am announcing today that the town airport will be renamed the Evelyn Sharp Field." Everyone applauded and cheered. Tears rolled down Nancy Batson's face.

September 12, 1948, while John and Mary Sharp drove to the landing strip at the Evelyn Sharp Field, their eyes scanned the crowd of more than a thousand people. "They came to honor our daughter." Mary spoke in awe and then turned to her husband. "We understood that Evelyn was special from the day we first took her into our arms. But I never dreamed she would be special to so many others."

The dedication of the 'Evelyn Sharp Field' became a true celebration. The high school chorus and band performed. Local and regional pilots as well as training schools demonstrated formation flying and acrobatic maneuvers. P-51s and B-26s were flown over the field in honor of Evelyn's Fifth Rating in aviation. Stunning the participants, the Nebraska Air National Guard flew their new F-80 jets from the Lincoln airbase and roared over the crowd. At the end of the ceremony, Mr. and Mrs. Sharp stepped up onto the stage and carried personal remembrances of Evelyn's flying career. The container was sealed, and then officials placed Evelyn Sharp's remembrances beneath the silver, six-foot blades of the P-38 propeller.

Later, the Nebraska State Historical Society positioned a highway marker at the entrance of the Evelyn Shape Field as a lasting tribute to the remarkable woman from small-town Nebraska.

CHAPTER 12

Breaking Barriers

Ironically, on July 5, 1943, the WFTD and the WAFS became one unit. Then all the women military pilots were designated as WASPs, and their official title would be Ferry Pilot. The pilots continued to fly the PT-19, BT-13, BT-15, A-20, B-17, B-25, C-47, P-38, and UC-78 airplanes. Their official base and training facility became New Castle Army Air Base in Wilmington, Delaware.

From September 1942 until December 1944, the special units of female pilots played a significant role in the America's war effort. Sadly, these units still had no official military standing. In their service to America, the pilots flew more than sixty million miles and transported all types of military aircraft across the nation and beyond. The female pilots took part in live anti-aircraft gun practice and simulated strafing missions. As a result, thirty-eight female pilots were killed in the line of duty. One became lost and presumed killed while on a ferry mission during the Second World War. The female pilots' service freed-up male pilots to be available for military combat or other duties.

In December 1944, the two groups of patriot women were unceremoniously disbanded without any thanks or appreciation. At first it seemed these brave women would fade into history without recognition for their service to America. However, women who followed would not allow the trail blazers to be forgotten. Websites, books, articles have been written to honor the resilient, female pilots who broke stereotypes and limitations. Evelyn Sharp is an example of someone who didn't come from wealth or fame. However, this small-town Nebraska girl became an important person in American history. Her service during World War II was invaluable as she and her fellow women pilots prepared men to fly into battle. Evelyn and her comrades faced risks each day without equal pay and recognition.

Female aviators were finally granted veteran status for their service in 1977. That November, President Jimmy Carter signed a bill granting World War II Veterans status for former WASPs. Family members feel that the greatest tribute came on December 7, 1944, when General Arnold spoke before the last WASPs graduating class. "You . . . have shown that you can fly wingtip to wingtip with your brothers. If ever there was a doubt in anyone's mind that women could become skilled pilots, the WASPs dispelled that doubt. I want to stress how valuable I believe the whole WASP program has been for our country."

Evelyn's hometown of Ord, Nebraska celebrates Evelyn Sharp Days each June. Eventually Evelyn was introduced into the Nebraska Aviation Hall of Fame in 1992. Later, in 2018, Cumberland County, Pennsylvania – at the site of Evelyn's crash – dedicated a memorial at the Pfeiffer Memorial Arboretum and Nature Preserve.

"Follow your dreams. Keep your "head in the clouds!" Sharp was also awarded the Congressional Gold Medal recognizing her aviation contributions.

Evelyn Sharp would be embarrassed over all the fanfare that she deserves. She is an example to all young girls that determination and perseverance are the tools young women must use to become whatever and whomever they wish.

CHAPTER 13

More Opportunities to Learn about Evelyn Sharp

Bartels, D.R.A. (1996). Sharpie the life story of Evelyn Sharp. Lincoln, NE: Dageford Publishing.

Bartels, Diane Ruth Armour. Sharpie, The Life Story of Evelyn Sharp Nebraska's Aviatrix, 1996, Dageford Publishing, Lincoln, Nebraska.

Cole, Jean Hascall, Women Pilots of World War II, 1992, University of Utah Press, Salt Lake City.

Explore Nebraska History. "Evelyn Sharp." Accessed December 16, 2020, https://mynehistory.com/items/show/505.Evelyn Sharp - NVTN (natlvtn.org)

Furgurson, Ernest B. "America's First Women Aviators." America's First Women Aviators (historynet.com)

Gant, Kelli. "Women Involved in Aviation." Our History | 99s in Aviation History | Women in Involved Aviation (The Ninety-Nines, Inc.) (ninety-nines.org)

Goyer, Mireille. "Five decades of American female pilots' statistics. How did we do?" Five decades of U.S. Female Pilots Statistics (womenofaviationweek.org) January 28, 2021

Keil, Sally Van Wagenen. Those Wonderful Women in Their Flying Machines, 1979, Four Directions Press, New York

Landdeck, Katherine Sharp. The Women with Silver Wings, 2020, Crown, New York.

Lukesh, Dr. Jean A. Sky Rider, the Story of Evelyn Sharp, 2011, Field Mouse Productions, Grand Island/Palmer, Nebraska

Mason, Heather. "On This Day: Blanche Stuart Scott is the first female American pilot to make a public flight." https://amysmartgirls.com/on-this-day-blanche-stuart-scott-is-the-first-female-american-pilot-to-make-a-public-flight.

McKee, James. "Sharpie' Sharp, arguably Nebraska's most ..." Lincoln Journal Star. https://journalstar.com/news/local/jim-mckee/Evelyn '

Pappas, C. (2001). More notable Nebraskans. Lincoln, NE: Media Production and Marketing, Inc slang - Bing, January 8, 2021

Suciu, Peter. "Remember the WASPs: The Forgotten American Female Pilots of World War II." https://nationalinterest.org/blog/buzz/remember-wasps-forgotten-american-female-pilots-world-war-iiValley County | Ord, Nebraska History, January 2, 2021

Verges, Marianne. <u>On Silver Wings</u>, 1991, Ballantine Books, New York

"Women in Aviation History | Sharpie: The Life Story of Evelyn Sharp" - Nebraska's Aviatrix (The Ninety-Nines, Inc.) (ninety-nines.org)

CHAPTER 14

Books by Glenda K Clare

<u>Women Of Dust and Wind - The Hands and
Hearts Of Survival: Women Of the Dust Bowl</u>

During the Dust Bowl and Great Depression, the women of the home – wives and mothers - worked to help their family survive. Searching for food and learning to live on little money, the struggled to feed their families. But most of all, the fought the dust and wind. Dirt seeped into any crevice of the house. Dust blew through the cracks of the windows. Dust covered the babies' mouths forcing them to cough up black soil in the mornings. She dreams of a fairy tale marriage and a world that will match all her hopes. However during the 1930's and 1940's, nature challenges the Midwest with grasshoppers, dust, and drought. Strong women, like Lydia, found a way for their family to survive.

#425 in Teen & Young Adult Clean & Wholesome Romance

eBooks

#1,126 in Teen & Young Adult Historical Romance

#1,260 in History eBooks of Women

The Legacy of Prairie Winds

Sixteen-year-old Johann Gehring accepts a sponsorship to work for a cousin in Nebraska and leaves his family in Germany to find his destiny. He travels by train and then endures the hardships of traveling a ship from Germany to America in search of his dreams. The Crystal Castle welcomes him into a strange world, but thankfully, his sponsor has sent him a train ticket to Antelope County in Nebraska. Challenged by the never-ending wind, rolling, treeless hills, and a lonely life on the prairie, Johann and his sponsor struggle to stay the course and make a home on the Nebraska plains. Johann learns to dig a well, build a sod house, and preserve strange new foods. But nature is the strongest foe sending tornados, prairie fires, and freezing winters. Romance and love fill Johann's life when he courts the beautiful but determined Helena. During their marriage, they raise five independent children including the headstrong, Berta.

#561 in Teen & Young Adult Clean & Wholesome Romance eBooks

#1,481 in Teen & Young Adult Historical Romance

#1,933 in History eBooks of Women

Time For Courage: Surviving Yellowstone

Sixteen-year-old Seth knew that his classmates considered him too serious and a nerd. But Seth knew differently, 'That's just not who

I am.' Seth was aware of his strengths especially his knowledge of Yellowstone and its caldera of more than fifteen-hundred square miles. 'What will happen if the geysers got out of whack and over-heated? Would the volcano erupt?' The Chambers had planned for their family camping trip to Yellowstone Park for months and hoped this trip would create memories. They had no idea how their lives would be changed.

#115 in Teen & Young Adult Nonfiction on Peer Pressure

#2,243 in Two-Hour Teen & Young Adult Short Reads

#2,670 in Two-Hour Science Fiction & Fantasy Short Reads

CHAPTER 15

About Glenda K Clare

FAITHFULLY WRITING WITH INTEGRITY, VISION, AND EMOTION TO TOUCH THE SOUL AND HEART OF MY READERS.

From an early age sitting on the arm of her grandmother's rocking chair, she loved reading. Reading and writing were survival tools in bad times and avenues for creativity in lonely times.
She encourages anyone - no matter her age - to write and share the inspiring ideas living in her brain and heart. Glenda taught English Literature and creative writing to high school and middle. She was constantly amazed at the creativity of young people. Now retired, her dream is now to focus on her own writing and has been awarded the Bess Streeter Aldrich Short Story Award.

9 798223 859376